NATIONAL ANTHEMS OF THE WORLD

NATIONAL ANTHEMS
of the
WORLD

Edited by

MARTIN SHAW, HENRY COLEMAN
and T. M. CARTLEDGE

LONDON

BLANDFORD PRESS

First published in 1960
Second and revised edition 1963
Third and revised edition 1969

© Copyright 1969 by Blandford Press Ltd.
167 High Holborn, W.C.1

SBN 7137 02672

MADE IN GREAT BRITAIN

Engraved and printed by Lowe and Brydone (Printers) Ltd.,
Victoria Road, London, N.W.10
Bound by Richard Clay and Co. Ltd., Bungay, Suffolk

CONTENTS

Preface and Acknowledgments vii

A

Abu Dhabi 9
Abyssinia (see Ethiopia)
Afghanistan . . . 10
Albania 11
Algeria 13
Andorra 17
Argentine 20
Australia 26
Austria 28

B

Bahrain 30
Barbados 31
Belgium 34
Bolivia 39
Botswana 44
Brazil 45
Brunei 52
Bulgaria 54
Burma 58

C

Cambodia 60
Cameroon 63
Canada 67
Central African Republic . 71
Ceylon 74
Chad 78
Chile 81
China 88
Colombia 92
Congo (Brazzaville) . . 96
Congo (Kinshasa) . . 99
Costa Rica . . . 104
Cuba 108
Czechoslovakia . . . 111

D

Danomey 114
Denmark 118
Dominican Republic . . 122

E

Ecuador . . . 126
Egypt (see United Arab Republic)
Eire 132
El Salvador . . . 136
Estonia 144
Ethiopia 146

F

Faroe Islands . . . 148
Finland 151
France 153

G

Gabon 156
Gambia, The . . . 160
Germany 162
Ghana 164
Great Britain . . . 166
Greece 167
Greenland 170
Guatemala 172
Guinea 176
Guyana 177

H

Haiti 179
Honduras 182
Hungary 187

I

Iceland 189
India 191
Indonesia 196
Iran 201
Iraq 204
Irish Republic (see Eire)
Isle of Man . . . 205
Israel 206
Italy 208
Ivory Coast . . . 212

J

Jamaica 215
Japan 217
Johore 218
Jordan 220

K

Kenya 221
Korea 223
Kuwait 225

L

Laos 226
Latvia 229
Lebanon 231
Lesotho 234
Liberia 235
Libya 238

A*

Liechtenstein . . . 242
Lithuania 244
Luxembourg . . . 246

M

Madagascar (Malagasy) . 248
Malawi 250
Malaysia 253
Maldive Islands . . . 255
Mali 257
Malta 261
Mauritania 263
Mauritius 266
Mexico 268
Monaco 273
Mongolia 275
Morocco 276
Muscat and Oman . . 278

N

Nepal 280
Netherlands . . . 282
Netherlands Antilles . . 284
Newfoundland . . . 285
New Zealand . . . 287
Nicaragua 291
Niger 294
Nigeria 299
Norway 300

P

Pakistan 303
Panama 306
Paraguay 310
Peru 315
Philippines, The . . . 320
Poland 325
Portugal 327
Puerto Rico . . . 331

Q

Qatar 332

R

Romania 333
Rwanda 340

S

Sabah 343
San Marino . . . 345
Saudi Arabia . . . 347
Senegal 348
Sierra Leone . . . 352
Singapore 354

Somalia 356
South Africa . . . 357
(see also Nkosi Sikelel'i
Africa) 451
Southern Yemen . . 361
Spain 362
Sudan 363
Surinam 366
Swaziland 368
Sweden 371
Switzerland . . . 373
Syria 381

T

Tanzania 383
Thailand 385
Tibet 387
Togo 390
Tonga 393
Trinidad and Tobago . . 395
Tunisia 397
Turkey 402

U

Uganda 404
Ukraine 405
Union of Socialist Soviet Re-
publics 408
United Arab Republic . . 411
United Kingdom of Great
Britain and Northern Ire-
land (see Great Britain)
United States of America . 414
Upper Volta . . . 417
Uruguay 419

V

Vatican 426
Venezuela 430
Viet-Nam 433

W

Wales 436
Western Samoa . . . 438

Y

Yemen 441
Yugoslavia 444

Z

Zambia 449

Appendix
Nkosi Sikelel'i Africa . . 451

NATIONAL DAYS . . 453

Publisher's Preface and Acknowledgments

THE WORLD-WIDE RESPONSE to the first and second editions of this book has given the opportunity now of including in this third edition a further 19 anthems: these are mainly the National Anthems of countries which have achieved independence since 1963, and there are some additional National Anthems not included in the previous editions. There have also been one or two changes: Bulgaria has a new National Anthem; Netherlands Antilles now has an official National Anthem and no longer uses the anthem of Curacao included in the second edition of this book. The National Song " The Maple Leaf for Ever " is no longer used in Canada, and has been omitted. A number of amendments have been made to anthems previously printed.

For the new anthems we are indebted to the Embassies and their staffs who have supplied much of the information; to the Royal Marine School of Music, for their close liaison and consultation; and particularly to Dr. W. L. Reed, who has been responsible for a number of the revisions and some of the arrangements of the new anthems.

The original idea for this book came from J. B. Cramer & Co. Ltd. who published a wartime collection of *National Anthems of the United Nations* edited by Martin Shaw. Upon the death of Dr. Shaw in 1959, the musical editorship of *National Anthems of the World* was taken over by Dr. Henry Coleman. Upon Dr. Coleman's death in 1965, Dr. T. M. Cartledge, who had worked with him on the first and second editions, became musical editor.

Acknowledgement is made at the foot of those anthems which are the copyright of J. B. Cramer & Co. Ltd. and other copyright material has been similarly acknowledged. Every effort has been made to trace copyright ownership, and it is regretted if any acknowledgements have been unwittingly omitted. In most cases the version in the melody and the accompaniment is that officially authorized by the State. Where piano arrangements and translations have been specially made, these may not be reproduced without the permission of Blandford Press Ltd.

Certain National Anthems have numerous verses, only one or two of which are customarily used, and so only these are given. Where English translations have been versified to fit the music, this has been done not so much for the purpose of singing (for the original language or languages would be used), but more to offer an indication of the meaning and so help in intelligent interpretation in singing the original words.

Where an anthem is in a language that is not written in the Latin alphabet, the words are given in a transliterated phonetic version to enable the anthem to be sung by those who cannot read it in its original form. This applies to the following:

Bulgaria	Jordan	Sudan
Burma	Laos	Syria
Cambodia	Lebanon	Thailand
China	Libya	Tibet
India	Maldive Islands	Tunisia
Israel	Muscat and Oman	United Arab Republic
Japan	Pakistan	U.S.S.R.
		Yemen

We acknowledge the work of Mr. Na'im Al-Basri who helped in the preparation of the musical arrangements of Libya, Jordan and Yemen and in the transliterated phonetic versions and translations of these and other Arabic countries.

We must also acknowledge the help of many officials and individuals all over the world who have given much information on important details. They are too numerous to list individually. Mention must, however, be made of Mr. Michael Karl Blackshaw, who put at our disposal material which he had assembled for a book on the same subject.

On various occasions we have consulted the Foreign Office, the Admiralty, the War Office, the BBC Music Library and the Royal Military School of Music, Kneller Hall, and acknowledge their assistance.

The main reference books consulted are Paul Nettl's *National Anthems* (1952, Storm Publishers, New York), Grove's *Dictionary of Music* (Macmillan), Collier's Encyclopedia (1959, New York), Murillo's *National Anthems of Countries of North, Central and South America* (1935).

Countries which are the dependent territories of other countries principally use the National Anthem of the " mother country." Where a country has in addition its own National Song which is used on important occasions, this is also given.

The final selection of anthems for such a volume as this must involve in some instances political and diplomatic implications, and the decision over this selection is that of the publisher.

It is hoped that this third edition of *National Anthems of the World* will continue to be a useful source book, not only for the increasing number of occasions on which it is desired to sing or play a particular anthem, but also as a reference book of considerable interest (as it has already proved) and as a record of the aspirations of the whole family of nations epitomised in the verses of these anthems.

ABU DHABI

Music by
LT. ISHAK SOLIMAN
Harmonised by
W. L. REED

AFGHANISTAN

No words

Music by
MOHAMMED FARUKH
Arr. by MOHAMMED MOKHTAR

Adopted as National Anthem, 1943

ALBANIA
Hymni i Flamurit

Words by
ASDREN (A.S. DRENOVA)

Melody by
CIPRIAN PORUMBESCU (1880)
Arr. by HENRY COLEMAN

Rreth flam - ur - it të për ba - shku - ar Me - një dë - shir e një që - llim; Të gjith at - je duk 'ju be - tu - ar Të lid - him be - sën për shpë - tim. Prej

Adopted as National Anthem, 1912

luf - te veç a - y lar - go - - het, Që ë-shtë lin - dur tra - dhë -

- tor, Kush ë - shtë bu - rrë nuk fri-ko - het, Po

vdes, po vdes si një dë - shmor. Prej - shmor.

Free Translation

The flag which in battle unites us
Found us all ready for the oath,
One mind, one aim, until our land
Becomes free from the enemy.
We stand in the battle for right and freedom,
The enemies of the people stand alone,
The hero dedicates his life to our land,
Even in dying he will be brave.

ALGERIA
Qassaman

Words by
MUFDI ZAKARIA

Music by
MOHAMED FAWZI
Arr. by TAREK HASSAN

Qa - ssa - man   Bin - na - zi - la - t Il - ma - hi - qat ____   Wad - di -
- maa   Iz - za - ki - ya - t It - ta - hi - rat. ____   Qa - ssa -

Mufdi Zakara, who wrote the words, is a celebrated contemporary Algerian poet;
Mohamed Fawzi is an Egyptian musician.

Wal - bo - noo - d Il - la - mi - aa - t Il - kha - fi - qa - t F'Il - gi

bal Ish - sha - mi - kha - t Ish sha - hi - qa - t Nah - no Thur - na Fa ha -

-ya - ton Aw ma ma - at Wa A - qad - na Al - az - ma An Tah - ya Al - ga -

-za - ir Fash - ha - doo Fash - ha - doo Fash - ha - doo.

2. *Nah-no Gon-don Fi Sa-bi-l Il hakki Thor-na*
Wa I-la Iss-tiq-la-li-na Bil-har-bi Kum-na.
Lam Ya-kon Yoss-gha La-na Lam-ma Na-tak-na
Fat-ta-khath-na Ran-na-t Al-ba-roo-di Waz-na.
Wa Azaf-na Na-gha-ma-t Al-rash-sha-shi Lah-na
Wa A-qad-na Al-azma An Tah-ya Al-ga-za-ir.
   Fash-ha-doo! Fash-ha-doo! Fash-ha-doo!

3. *Nah-no min Ab-ta-li-na Nad-fa-oo Gon-dan*
Wa A-la Ash-la-ina Nass-na-oo Mag-dan.
Wa A-la Ar-wa-he-na Nass-a-do Khul-dan
Wa A-la Ha-ma-ti-na Nar-fa-o Ban-dan.
Gab-ha-to 'L-tah-ree-ri Aa-tay-na-ki Ah-dan
Wa A-qad-na Al-azma An Tah-ya Al-ga-za-ir.
   Fash-ha-doo! Fash-ha-doo! Fash-ha-doo!

4. *Sar-kha-to 'l-aw-ta-ni min Sa-h Il-fi-da*
Iss-ma-oo-ha Wass-ta-gee-bo Lin-ni-da
Wak-to-boo-ha Bi-di-maa Il-sho-ha-daa
Wak-ra-oo-ha Li-ba-ny Il-geeli gha-dan.
Kad Ma-dad-na La-ka Ya Mag-do Ya-da
Wa A-qad-na Al-azma An Tah-ya Al-ga-za-ir.
   Fash-ha-doo! Fash-ha-doo! Fash-ha-doo!

French Translation

1. *Par les foudres qui anéantissent,*
Par les flots de sang pur et sans tache,
Par les drapeaux flottants qui flottent,
Sur les hauts djebels orgueilleux et fiers,
Nous jurons nous être révoltés pour vivre ou pour mourir,
Et nous avons juré de mourir pour que vive l'Algérie!*
   Témoignez! Témoignez! Témoignez!

2. *Nous sommes des soldats pour la justice, révoltés,*
Et pour notre indépendance nous avons engagé le combat,
Nous n'avons obéi à nulle injonction en nous soulevant.
Le bruit de la poudre a été notre mesure
Et le crépitement des mitrailleuses notre chant favori.
Et nous avons juré de mourir pour que vive l'Algérie!
   Témoignez! Témoignez! Témoignez!

3. *Sur nos héros nous bâtirons une gloire*
Et sur nos corps nous monterons à l'immortalité,
Sur nos âmes, nous construirons une armée
Et de notre espoir nous lèverons l'étendard.
Front de la libération, nous t'avons prêté serment
Et nous avons juré de mourir pour que vive l'Algérie!
   Témoignez! Témoignez! Témoignez!

4. *Le cri de la patrie monte des champs de bataille.*
Ecoutez-le et répondez à l'appel.
Ecrivez-le dans le sang des martyrs
Et dictez-le aux générations futures.
Nous t'avons donné la main, ô gloire,
Et nous avons juré de mourir pour que vive l'Algérie!
   Témoignez! Témoignez! Témoignez!

* litt. "SERMENT" peut se traduire par "Nous jurons" ou "nous avons juré".

English Translation by T. M. Cartledge.
(from the French)

1. We swear by the lightning that destroys,
   By the streams of generous blood being shed,
   By the bright flags that wave,
   Flying proudly on the high djebels,
   That we are in revolt, whether to live or to die,
       We are determined that Algeria should live,
       So be our witness– be our witness– be our witness.

2. We are soldiers in revolt for truth
   And through war we try to get our Independence.
   When we spoke, nobody listened to us,
   So we have taken the noise of gunpowder as our rhythm
   And the sound of machine-guns as our melody,
       We are determined that Algeria should live,
       So be our witness– be our witness– be our witness.

3. From our heroes we shall make an army come to being,
   From our dead we shall build up a glory,
   Our spirits shall ascend to immortality
   And on our shoulders we shall raise the Standard.
   To the nation's Liberation Front we have sworn an oath
       We are determined that Algeria should live,
       So be our witness– be our witness– be our witness.

4. The cry of the Fatherland sounds from the battle-fields.
   Listen to it and answer the call!
   Let it be written with the blood of martyrs
   And be read to future generations.
   Oh, Glory, we have held out our hand to you
       We are determined that Algeria should live,
       So be our witness– be our witness– be our witness.

ANDORRA

Words by
The Hon. Dr. D. JOAN BENLLOCH I VIVÓ

Music by
Father ENRIC MARFANY

El gran Car - le-many, mon Pa - - re, dels a- -larbs me des - lliu - rá, _____ i del cel vi - da em do- -ná _____ de Me - rit - xell la gran Ma - re. Prin-

This became officially the National Anthem on the 8th September 1914,
the anniversary day of the Jungfrau von Meritxell, patron saint of Andorra.

-ce - sa nasqui i Pu - bi - lla en - tre dos na - cions neu-

-tral;_____ Sols res - to l'ú - ni - ca fi - lla del im-

-pe - ri Car - le - many. Cre - ient i lliu - re on - se

se - gles, cre - ient i lliu - re vull ser.

Free Translation

The great Charlemagne, my Father, from the Saracens liberated me,
and from heaven he gave me life of Meritxell the great Mother. I was
born a Princess, a Maiden neutral between two nations; I am the only
remaining daughter of the Carolingian empire. Believing and free
eleven centuries, believing and free I will be. The laws of the land be
my tutors and my defender Princes! and my defender Princes!

ARGENTINE

Words by
VICENTE LÓPEZ Y PLANES
(1784-1856)

Music by
BLAS PARERA (b. 1777)
Arr. by
JUAN PEDRO ESNAOLA (1808-1878)

Officially adopted as National Anthem, 11th May 1813, by the General Constituent Assembly of Argentina

rui - do de ro - tas ca - de - nas; Ved en

tro - na a la no - ble I-gual-dad.

¡Ya__ su tro - no dig-ní - si-mo a-brie - ron Las Pro-

-vin - cias U - ni - das del Sud! Y los

li - bres del mun - do res - pon - den: ¡Al gran

pue - blo Ar - gen - ti - no, Sa - lud!_____ ¡Al gran

pue - blo Ar - gen - ti - no, Sa - lud! Y___ los

li - bres del mun - do res - pon - den ¡Al gran

pue - blo Ar-gen - ti - no, Sa - lud! Y___ los

li - bres del mun - do res - pon - den ¡Al gran

pue - blo Ar-gen - ti - no, Sa - lud!

CHORUS
Allegro vivace

Sean e - ter - nos los lau - re - les. Que su - pi - mos con - se -

- guir: Que su - pi - mos con - se - guir: Co - ro -

Lento

lunga

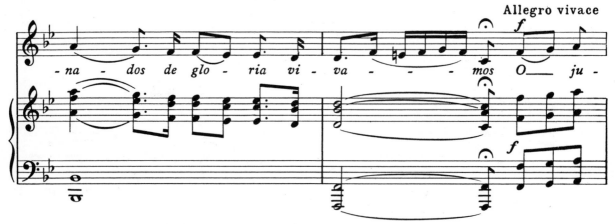

- na - dos de glo - ria vi - va - - mos O ju -

Allegro vivace

- re - mos con glo - ria mo - rir. O ju -

-re - mos con glo - ria mo - rir. O ju -

-re - mos con glo - ria mo - rir.

Free Translation

Hear, oh mortals! the sacred cry:
Freedom, freedom, freedom!
Hear the noise of broken chains;
See the throne of Equality the noble.

The United Provinces of the South
Their throne full of dignity opened!
And the free of the world reply:
A salutation to the great Argentine people!

CHORUS Let those laurels be eternal
Which we knew how to win:
Let us live crowned by glory
Or swear with glory to die.

AUSTRALIA

Advance Australia Fair

Words and Music by
PETER DODDS McCORMICK
("AMICUS") (1834-1916)
Arr. by H.A. CHAMBERS

Maestoso

1. Aus - tra - lia's sons, let us re - joice, For we are young and free; We've
2. When gal - lant Cook from Al - bion sail'd, To trace wide o - ceans o'er, True
3. While o - ther na - tions of the globe Be - hold us from a - far, We'll
4. Should for - eign foe e'er sight our coast Or dare a foot to land, We'll

gold - en soil and wealth for toil, Our home is girt by sea. Our
Brit - ish cour - age bore him on Till he land - ed on our shore. Then
rise to high re - nown and shine Like our glo - rious south - ern star. From
rouse to arms like sires of yore To guard our na - tive strand. Bri -

"God Save the Queen" is the National Anthem. No other anthem has
been officially adopted, yet some Australians regard "Advance Australia Fair" in this light. This is played as a signature tune at some
Australian Radio Stations and T.V. Channels.
Copyright W.H. Paling & Co. Ltd., Sydney

land a-bounds in Na-ture's gifts Of beau-ty rich and rare; In
here he raised old Eng-land's flag, The stan-dard of the brave; With
Eng-land, Sco - tia, E - rin's Isle, Who come our lot to share, Let
tan - nia then shall sure - ly know, Be - yond wide o - cean's roll Her

his - t'ry's page let ev - 'ry stage Ad - vance Aus-tra - lia fair.
all her faults we love her still—"Bri - tan - nia rules the wave."
all com - bine with heart and hand To ad - vance Aus-tra - lia fair.
sons in fair Aus - tra - lia's land Still keep a Brit - ish soul.

CHORUS (S.A.T.B.)

In joy - ful strains then let us sing, "Ad - vance Aus-tra - lia fair."

AUSTRIA

Words by
PAULA PRERADOVIĆ (b.1887)

Music by
WOLFGANG AMADEUS MOZART (1756-1791)
Arr. by VIKTOR KELDORFER

1. Land der Ber - ge, Land am Stro - me, Land der
2. Heiß um feh - det, wild um strit - ten, liegst dem

Äk - ker, Land der Do - me, Land der Häm - mer,
Erd - teil du in - mit - ten ei - nem star - ken

zu - kunfts - reich! Hei - mat bist du gro - ßer Söh - ne,
Her - zen gleich. Hast seit frü - hen Ah - nen - ta - gen

Officially adopted as National Anthem by Austrian Cabinet 22nd October, 1946

3. *Mutig in die neuen Zeiten,*
   frei und gläubig sieh uns schreiten,
   arbeitsfroh und hoffnungsreich.
   Einig laß in Brüderchören,
   Vaterland, dir Treue schwören,
   Vielgeliebtes Österreich. (bis)

Free Translation

1. Land of mountains, land of streams, land of fields,
   land of spires, land of hammers, with a rich future,
   you are the home of great sons, a nation blessed by
   its sense of beauty,
   highly praised Austria, highly praised Austria.

2. Strongly fought for, fiercely contested, you are in
   the centre of the Continent like a strong heart, you
   have borne since the earliest days the burden of a
   high mission,
   much tried Austria, much tried Austria.

3. Watch us striding free and believing, with courage, into
   new eras, working cheerfully and full of hope, in
   fraternal chorus let us take in unity the oath of
   allegiance to you, our country,
   our much beloved Austria, our much beloved Austria.

BAHRAIN

QATAR

BARBADOS

Words by
IRVINE BURGIE

Music by
VAN ROLAND EDWARDS

1. In — plen-ty and in time of need When this fair land was young, Our — brave fore-fa-thers sowed the seed From which our pride is sprung, A pride that makes no wan-ton boast Of what it has with —

2. The — Lord has been the peo-ple's guide For past three hun-dred years. With — Him still on the peo-ple's side We have no doubts or fears. Up-ward and on-ward we shall go, In-spired, ex-ult-ing,

This anthem was adopted on 30th November, 1966, when Barbados attained Independence.

stood, That binds our hearts from coast to coast— The
free, And great - er will our na - tion grow In

CHORUS

pride of na - tion - hood. We loy - al sons and
strength and u - ni - ty.

daugh - ters all Do here - by make it known These

fields and hills be - yond re - call Are now our ve - ry

own. We write our names on his - tory's page With

ex - pec - ta - tions great, Strict guard - ians of our

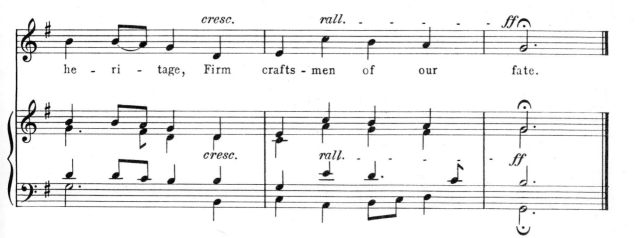

he - ri - tage, Firm crafts - men of our fate.

BELGIUM
La Brabançonne

Words by
"JENNEVAL" (Hyppolite Dechet)
Last verse by
CHARLES ROGIER (1800-1885)
English translation by
MARY ELIZABETH SHAW and DICCON SHAW

Music by
FRANÇOIS VAN CAMPENHOUT (1779-1848)

1. O Va-der-land, o __ e-del land der Bel __ gen, Zoo mach-tig
1. A-près des siè-cles __ d'es-cla-va __ ge, Le
1. From out the tomb of __ bon-dage and sla-ver-y __ Has __

steeds __ door moed en werk-zaam-heid, __ De we-reld
Bel-ge, sor-tant du tom-beau, __
Bel-gium at last ris-en free; __

ziet ver-won-derd u we tel __ gen Aan't hoofd van
A re-con-quis par son cou-ra __ ge Son __
And has re-cov-ered by her bra-ver-y, Her __

Written and composed in 1830 during the struggle between Belgium
and Holland for the independence of Belgium. Revised in 1951, when
the Flemish version replaced existing Flemish National Anthem.

By permission of J.B.Cramer & Co.Ltd.

kunst, van han - del, nij - ver - heid! De vrij - heids-
nom, ses droits____ et son dra - peau! Et ta
name, her flag,____ her lib - er - ty; And by your

-zon giet licht op u - we we - gen, En on - be-
main sou - ve - raine____ et____ fiè - re, Peu-
mien un - daunt - ed and vic - tor - ious Since that

-vreesd____ staart gij de toe - komst aan! Gij mint uw
-ple dé - sor - mais____ in - domp - té, Gra -
day,____ up - hold - ing your cause, Is bla - zoned

vorst;   *zijn lief - de stroomt u te - gen,*   *Zijn hand ge-*
-va   *sur ta vieil - le ban - niè - re*   *Le*
on   your an - cient ban - ner glor - ious   Your

-leidt _____ *u op uw glo - rie - baan,*   *Gij mint uw*
Roi, _____ *la loi, la li - ber - té!*   *Gra -*
King, _____ your free - dom and your laws.   Is bla - zoned

vorst;   *zijn lief - de stroomt u te - gen,*   *Zijn hand ge-*
-va   *sur ta vieil - le ban - niè - re*   *Le*
on   your an - cient ban - ner glo - ious,   Your

-leidt _____ u op uw glo - rie baan,   *Zijn hand ge-*
Roi, _____ la loi, la li - ber - té!   *Le* _____
King, _____ your free - dom and your laws.   Your _____

-leidt _____ u op uw glo - rie baan,   *Zijn hand ge-*
Roi, _____ la loi, la li - ber - té!   *Le* _____
King, _____ your free - dom and your laws.   Your _____

-leidt _____ u op uw glo - rie baan. _____
Roi, _____ la loi, la li - ber - té! _____
King, _____ your free - dom and your laws. _____

FLEMISH

2. Woei eens de storm ons toe uit vreemde streken,
  Blijft Vlaming, Waal, vereend met hart en ziel;
Ons voorgeslacht heeft nooit een stap geweken,
  Maar streed met moed en zegepraalde of viel!
Het roept ons toe: Bewaart 't erf uwer vaad'ren
  Bewaart uw roem; uw eendracht zij uw macht!
O luistert nooit naar lafaards en verraad'ren,
  Weg met al wie het Vaderland veracht.

3. Aan 't fiere land, waarvoor ons vaad'ren streden,
  Behoort ons hart, behoort ons goed en bloed!
Werd ooit de grens door vreemden overschreden,
  Wij schoten toe met Vlaamschen heldenmoed!
Laat overal 't driekleurig vaandel wapp'ren
  In dorp en stad, bij burger en soldaat.
Dat zinnebeeld is heilig voor de dapp'ren:
  Wee hem die 't ooit wou schennen of versmaadt.

FRENCH

2. Marche de ton pas énergique,
  Marche de progrès en progrès;
Dieu, qui protège la Belgique,
  Sourit à tes mâles succès.
Travaillons: notre labeur donne
  A nos champs la fécondité,
Et la splendeur des arts couronne
  Le Roi, la loi, la liberté.

3. O Belgique, ô mère chérie,
  A toi nos cœurs, à toi nos bras,
A toi notre sang, ô Patrie,
  Nous le jurons tous, tu vivras!
Tu vivras toujours grande et belle,
  Et ton invincible unité
Aura pour devise immortelle:
  Le Roi, la loi, la liberté.

ENGLISH

2. March on! with steady unfailing paces
  From progress to progress march on.
Still, through misfortune, on your faces
  God's smile, protecting you, has shone.
Let us work! for labour, life-bestowing,
  From the earth her fertile produce draws,
And crowns, with splendour ever brightly glowing,
  Your King, your freedom and your laws.

3. Beloved Belgium, beloved Mother,
  Our arms, our hearts, our blood we give
Freely to you, and to none other;
  And by these we swear that you shall live.
Shall live in beauty and in strength for ever
  Holding fast, as watchword of your cause,
The deathless bond that binds your sons together
  Your King, your freedom and your laws.

BOLIVIA

Words by
JOSE IGNACIO de SANJINÉS
(1786-1864)
Translated by
G. H. HATCHMAN
Versified by
SEBASTIAN SHAW

Music by
BENEDETTO VINCENTI

Allegro marziale

VERSE

1. Bo - li - via - nos: el ha - do pro -
1. Oh Bo - li - via, our long felt de -

-pi - cio co - ro - nó nues - tros vo - tos y an - he - lo; es ya
-sires, By the kind - li - ness of des - ti - ny are crowned now. Here, where

Played for first time in 1842 and adopted the same year.
José de Sanjinés was a jurist and signer of the Bolivian Declaration of Independence.
By permission J.B. Cramer & Co. Ltd.

li - bre ya li - bre es - te sue - - lo, ya ce -
free - dom, our free - dom, is found now, E - ver from

-só su ser-vil___ con - di - ción. Al es -
bon - dage we cel - e - brate re - lease. Af - ter

-truen - do marcial que a - yer fue - - ra y al cla -
all the mar - tial clam - our that as - pires___ To the

-mor___ de la gue - rra ho - rro - ro - - so, si - guen
clash of war - fare's hi - de-ous in - sa - ni - ty, Now in

an - tes que es-cla - vos vi-vir!
death than ex-is - tence as slaves!

2. Esta tierra inocente y hermosa
que ha debido a Bolívar su nombre,
es la Patria feliz donde el hombre
goza el bien de la dicha y la paz.
Que los hijos del grande Bolívar
han ya mil y mil veces jurado
morir antes que ver humillado
de la Patria el augusto pendón.

CORO: De la Patria etc.

3. Loor eterno a los bravos guerreros
cuyo heróico valor y firmeza
conquistaron las glorias que empieza
hoy Bolivia feliz a gozar.
Que sus nombres el mármol y el bronce
a remotas edades trasmitan
y en sonoros cantares repitan
¡Libertad, Libertad, Libertad!

CORO: De la Patria etc.

2. Here where Justice has raised up her throne,
Long denied her by the evil of oppression,
Her flung banners find glorious expression
We are free, we are free, we are free!
Sons, whom mighty Bolivar shall call his own,
Have a thousand thousand times in great solemnity
Freely offered life itself as sworn indemnity,
If dishonoured their flag should ever be.

CHORUS: Evermore, Motherland etc.

3. Those brave warriors eternally praise,
Whose courage, unexampled, evermore is
The foundation of all the proud glories
To which happy Bolivia is heir.
Lettered bronze and marble gratefully we'll raise
That their deeds may live for distant generations,
And our sons' and grandsons' joyful salutations
Shall, in song, honour still the great names there.

CHORUS: Evermore, Motherland etc.

BOTSWANA
(Fatshe la rona)

Words and English translation by
K. T. MOTSETE, M.A., B.D.(London)

Music by
K. T. MOTSETE

Officially adopted 30 September 1966, when Botswana became independent.

BRAZIL

Words by
JOAQUIM OSÓRIO DUQUE ESTRADA
(1870–1927)
Translated by
GASTÃO NOTHMAN
Versified by
SEBASTIAN SHAW

Music by
FRANCESCO MANOEL da SILVA
(1795–1865)

The music was written for the National Anthem in 1831. In 1922 a new text was officially adopted and the same tune retained.

By permission of J.B.Cramer & Co.Ltd.

VERSE

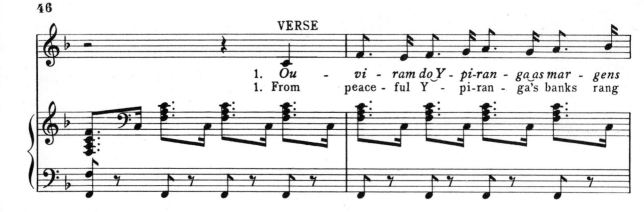

1. *Ou - vi - ram do Y - pi - ran - ga as mar - gens*
1. From peace - ful Y - pi - ran - ga's banks rang

plá - ci - das De um po - vo he - roi - co o bra - do re - tum -
out a cry, A chal - lenge from a peo - ple who were

- ban - te, E o sol da li - ber - da - de em rá - ios
fear - less; Thence - forth the sun of Free - dom climbed our

fúl - gi - dos, Bri - lhou no céu da Pá - tria nes - se in
coun - try's sky, And poured its rays up - on us, bright and

stan - te,   Se o pe - nhor____ des-sa i - gual - da - de   Con - se -
peer - less. We, with breasts bared,   de - fy, oh Free - dom,   Death it -

-gui - mos con - quis - tar com bra - ço   for - te,   Em teu
-self, for the e - qua - li - ty you taught us!   Striv - ing

sei - o,   Oh, Li - ber - da - de,   De - sa -
fierce - ly, here in your bo - som,   To be

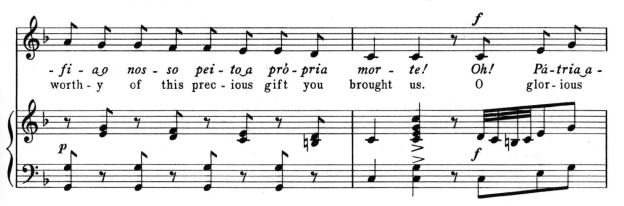

-fi - a o nos - so pei - to a pró - pria mor - te!   Oh! Pá - tria a -
worth - y of this prec - ious gift you brought us.   O   glor - ious

-ma-da, i-do-la-tra-da, Sal-ve! Sal - ve! Bra-
and be-lov-ed land, hail! Hail Bra- zil!_____ Be-

-sil, um so-nho in-ten-so um rå - io ví - vi - do De a-
-hold a won-drous vi - sion, lo! a dazz - ling ray Of

-mor e des - pe-ran - ça à ter - ra des - ce, Se em
love and hope, from heav'n to earth, trans-cen - dent! Our

teu for-mo - so céu, ri-so-nho e lím - pi - do, À i -
smil - ing skies, in lim - pid beau - ty, now dis - play À

-ma - gem do cru - zei - ro res - plan - de - ce. Gi -
war - rior's form, gi - gan - tic and res - plen - dent. Whence

- gan - te pe - la pró - pria na - tu - re - za, Es
spring such beau - ty, brave - ry and strength so rare? Oh!

be - lo es for - te im - pá - vi - do co - los - so. E o
might - y vis - ion, well we know that we sur - vey Our

CHORUS

teu fu - tu - ro es - pe - lha es - sa gran - de - za. Ter - ra a - do -
coun - try's fu - ture great - ness shown for us there. A - mongst a

-ra - da,   en-tre ou-tras mil, ės tu, Bra - sil, Oh! Pá-tria a-
thou - sand,   You ev - er will Be, oh Bra - zil, The one dear

-ma - da!   dos fi - lhos dês - te so-lo ės mãe   gen -
home - land!   Oh bount-eous mo - ther, with such love   you

1

-til,   Pá - tria a-ma - da,   Bra - sil!
fill   Your proud chil - dren,   Bra - zil!

2

-sil!
-zil!

2. Deitado eternamente em berço esplêndido,
    Ao som do mar e à luz do céu profundo,
    Fulguras, Brasil, florão da América,
    Iluminado ao sol do novo mundo.
    Do que a terra mais garrida
    Teus risonhos, lindos campos têm mais flores,
    Nossos bosques têm mais vida,
    Nossa vida no teu seio mais amores.
        Oh! Pátria amada, idolatrada,
        Salve! Salve!
    Brasil, de amor eterno seja o símbolo
    O lábaro que ostentas estrelado,
    E diga o verde louro dessa flâmula
    Paz no futuro e glória no passado.
    Mas, se ergues da justiça a clava forte
    Verás que um filho teu não foge à luta
    Nem teme quem te adora a própria morte.
        Terra adorada entre, outras mil, és tu, Brasil,
        Oh! Pátria amada! dos filhos dêste solo és mãe gentil,
        Pátria amada, Brasil!

2. To ocean's music, under skies of deepest blue,
    America's fair flower, fading never,
    In splendour you lie cradled. Oh Brazil, on you
    The sun of this New World shines down for ever!
    Oh, far more than in fair lands elsewhere,
    Your sweet pastures are bedecked with smiling blossom;
    Your vast woodlands a greater life share,
    And a deeper love we know within your bosom.
        Oh glorious and beloved land, hail! Hail Brazil!
    Then let your starry ensign never cease to fly,
    Symbolic of the love that fills your story;
    And let the verdant laurels on your pennon cry:-
    "In future peace and in the past great glory!"
    But if, in justice, you should raise your mighty sword,
    You shall not see a son of yours from battle flee,
    Nor shall he fear to die for you, whom he adored.
        Amongst a thousand,
        You ever will
        Be, oh Brazil,
        The one dear homeland!
        Oh bounteous mother, with such love you fill
        Your proud children, Brazil!

BRUNEI

Words by
PENGIRAN MAHOMED YUSEF bin
PENGIRAN HAJI ABDUL RAHIM

Music by
INCHE AWANG BESAR bin SAGAP
Arr. by HENRY COLEMAN

Moderato

Ya Al - lah lan - jut - kan lah u - si - a

Du - li tu - an - ku yang ma - ha mu - li - a

A - dil ber - dau - lat me - naung - i no - sa

This anthem was composed in 1947 through the initiative of a group of youths who decided that their country should have a National Anthem, and chose two of their number to write and compose it. It was officially adopted in 1951.

Me - mim - pin ra'a - yat ke - kal baha - gi - a;

Hi - dup sen - to - sa Ne - ga - ra dan Sul - tan,

I - la - hi se - la - mat - kan Bru - nei Da - rus sa - lam.

Free Translation

Oh God, Long Live our Majesty the Sultan;
Justice and Sovereignty in sheltering our
country and leading our people;
Prosperity to our Nation and Sultan.
God Save Brunei.

BULGARIA
Shoumi Maritsa

Music by
GABRIEL SEBEK
Arr. by HENRY COLEMAN

Marziale

1. Shou - mi Ma - ri - tsa o - kar - va - ve - na,

Pla - che vdo - vi - tsa, lyu - to ra - ne - na.

Marsh,_____ marsh,_____ s'ge - ne - ra - la na - sh,

This National Anthem dates from the year 1885, but is not at present sung inside Bulgaria.

V'boy da le - tim   i   vrag da po - be - dim!   -dim!

2.   *Balgarsky cheda, tsyal svyat vi gleda,*
     V' boy za pobeda, slavno da varvim.
         Marsh, marsh s' Generala nash,
         v'boy da letim i vrag da pobedim!

3.   *Lavat Balkansky,   v'boy velikansky,*
     s'ordi doushmansky, vodi ni krilat.
         Marsh, marsh s' Generala nash,
         v'boy da letim i vrag da pobedim!

English Translation

1.   Maritsa rushes, stained with blood,
     A widow wails, fiercely wounded.
         March, march, with our General,
         Let's fly into battle and crush the enemy!

2.   Bulgarians, the whole world beholds you.
     Into a winning battle, let's gloriously go.
         March, march, with our General,
         Let's fly into battle and crush the enemy!

3.   The Balkan lion leads us flying
     Into a gigantic battle with the enemy hordes.
         March, march, with our General,
         Let's fly into battle and crush the enemy!

BULGARIA

DEAR FATHERLAND

Old Melody

Andante maestoso (♩ = 66)

VERSE

1. Gor - da Sta - ra pla - nee - na, do ne-yee Doo - na - va see-ne-yee, slun - tse Tra-kee-ya o - grya - va nad Pe - ree - na pla - men - e-yee.
2. Pad - na ha bor - tsee bez-chet za na - ro - da nash lyu-bim. Ma-yee-ko, da-yee nee muzh-ka see - la put - ya eem da pro - dul - zheem!
3. Droozh - no, brat - ya Bul - ga - ree, s nas Mos - kva e v meer i v bo-yee! Par - tee - ya ve - lee - ka vo - dee nash - ee - ya po - bye - den stro-yee!

This was adopted in 1964, replacing the previous Republic anthem. "Bulgaria mila, zemya na gheroi." It is based on words and melody sung in Bulgaria for many years. A group of writers and musicians worked on these to form this anthem.

Notes: ◡ = blended into diphthong
Zh = as S in PLEASURE
U = very short, as O in MONEY
H = as CH in Scottish LOCH

CHORUS

Mee - la Ro - dee - no, (Ro - dee - no), tee see ze - men ra - yee,

tvo - yee - ta hu - bost, tvo - yee - ta pre - lest, ah, te nya - mat

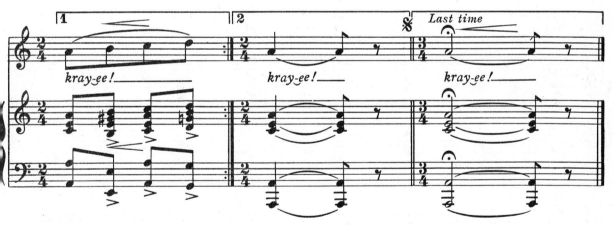

kray - ee! kray - ee! kray - ee!

1. Proudly rise the Balkan peaks,
   At their feet Blue Danube flows;
   Over Thrace the sun is shining,
   Pirin looms in purple glow.

       REFRAIN
           Oh, dear native land,
           Earthly paradise!
           For your loveliness, your beauty
           E'er will charm our eyes.

2. Countless warriors bravely fell
   For the people's sacred cause;
   Give us strength and firmness, Mother,
   Guide us on the road they chose.
                           REFRAIN

3. Be as one, Bulgarians!
   Moscow stands by us again;
   For our valiant Party leads us
   On to victory and fame!
                           REFRAIN

Translated by Katya Boyadjieva

D

BURMA

Words by
GROUP OF BURMESE
English versification by
T.M.CARTLEDGE

Music by
TH KIN BA THOUNG
Arr. by T. M. CARTLEDGE

Adagio

Gba ma - jay Bma py - ay
We shall love ev - er - more

do - bo bwa mway si mo chi mya - no bey.
Bur - ma, the land of our fath - ers of yore.

Byay daung-tsu go athé bay loo do ka kwe mlay.
Giv - ing our lives for our un - ion we fight.

This officially became the National Anthem in 1948.

* At the end of the anthem it is customary for the singers to give a slight bow.

CAMBODIA
Nokoreach

Words by
CHUON-NAT

Adapted from a Cambodian folk song
by F. PERRUCHOT and J. JEKYLL
Arr. by HENRY COLEMAN

1. Som pouk tep - da rak sa moha Khsath yeung_____ Oy ban roung roeung doy chey mon - kol___ srey sour - sdey Yeung Khnhom preah ang som chrok Krom moloup preah Ba - ro -

Adopted as the Royal and National Anthem, 1941, reaffirmed 1947

- mey_____ Ney preah No - rop - dey vong Khsat-tra del sang preah sat

thmâr Kroup Kraung dèn Kkmer bo-rann thkoeung thkann.2. Pra - sath sé-
3.Kroup vath a- kor.

2. *Prasath séla kombang kan dal prey*
   Kuor oy srâmay noeuk dâl yuos sak Moha Nokor
   Cheat Khmer dauch Thmar kong vong nôy lâar rung peung chom hor.
   Yeung sang Khim por pheap preng samnang robuos Kampuchea.
   Moha râth koeut mieñ you ang veanh hey.

3. *Kroup vath aram lû tè so sap thoeur*
   Sot doy am nô rom lik koun poth sasna
   Chol yeung chea neak thioeur thiak smos smak tam bêp donnta
   Kong tè thévoda nùng chuoy chrom chrèng phkôt phkang pra yoch oy
   Dol prateah Khmer chea Moha Nokor.

French Translation

1. *Que le ciel protège notre Roi*
   Et lui dispense le bonheur et la gloire.
   Qu'il règne sur nos cœurs et sur nos destinées
   Celui qui, héritier des Souverains bâtisseurs,
   Gouverne le fier et vieux Royaume.

2. *Les temples dorment dans la forêt*
   Rappelant la grandeur du Moha Nokor
   Comme le roc, la race khmère est éternelle
   Ayons confiance dans le sort du Campuchéa
   L'Empire qui défie les années.

3. *Les chants montent dans les pagodes*
   A la gloire de la Sainte foi Bouddhique.
   Soyons fidèles aux croyances de nos pères.
   Ainsi le ciel prodiguera-t-il tous ses bienfaits
   Au vieux pays khmer, le Moha Nokor.

English Translation

1. Heaven protects our King
   And gives Him happiness and glory
   To reign over our souls and our destinies
   The one being, heir of the Sovereign **constructors**
   Guiding the proud old Kingdom.

2. Temples are asleep in the forest
   Remembering the splendour of Moha Nokor.
   Like a rock the Khmer race is eternal.
   Let us trust in the fate of Campuchea
   The empire which challenges the ages.

3. Songs rise up from the pagodas,
   To the glory of holy buddhistic faith.
   Let us be faithful to our ancestors' belief.
   Thus heaven will lavish its bounty
   Towards the ancient Khmer country, the Moha Nokor.

CAMEROON

Chant de Ralliement

Words by RENE JAM AFAME
and a group of students
English versification by
T. M. CARTLEDGE

Music by
SAMUEL MINKYO BAMBA
and MOISE NYATE
Arr. by HENRY COLEMAN

1. O Ca - me - roun, ber - ceau de nos an -
2. Tu es la tom - be où dor - ment nos
1. O Ca - me - roon, that crad - led our fore -
2. You are the tomb where our fath - ers are

- cê - tres, Au - tre - fois tu vé - cus dans la bar - ba -
pè - res, Le jar - din que nos aï - eux ont cul - ti -
- fath - ers, In bar - bar - ic times you lived your ear - ly
rest - ing, You're the gar - den they pre-pared and they con -

This anthem was written and composed in 1928 by students from l'Ecole Normale de la
Mission Presbytérienne Américaine de Foulassi à Sangmelina, Cameroun. It was adopted as
the unofficial National Anthem in 1948 and became the official Anthem on 10th May, 1957

-rie.____ Comme un so - leil tu commences à pa -
-vé.____ Nous tra - vail - lons pour te ren - dre pros -
days. ____ But like the ris - ing ___ sun now ap -
-ceived.____ We work that you may be - come fair and

-raî - tre; Peu à peu tu sors de ta sau-va - ge -
-pè - re, Un beau jour en-fin nous se - rons ar - ri -
-pear - ing, Bit by bit you now are leav - ing sav - age
pros - p'rous, And one day at last we'll see it all a -

-ri - e. Que__ tous tes en-fants du__ Nord au Sud, De__
-vés. De l'A - fri-que soit fi - dèle en - fant Et
ways.___ May__ all your child-ren fol-low the com-mand, From__
-chieved.__ May you be a faith-ful child of Af - ri - ca, Advancing

l'Est à l'Ouest soient tout a - mour._____ Te ser - vir que ce soit__ leur__ seul_
pro-gres-se tou - jours en Paix,_____ Es-pé-rant que__ tes__ jeunes en -
East and West to give their heart,_____ Their on - ly wish_ to__ serve their
stead-i - ly__ in__ peace,_____ In hope that ev - 'ry young child_ of_

but Et_____ rem - plir leur de - voir tou-jours.
-fants T'ai - me - ront sans bornes à ja - mais.
land And with con - stan - cy all play their part.
yours Will__ love you un - til time_ shall_ cease.

CHORUS

Chère Pa - tri - - e, terre ché - ri - - e, Tu
This our land that we all love so, On

es no - tre seul et vrai bon - heur. No - tre
you our whole hap - pi - ness is stayed. You're our

joi - e, no - tre vi - e, A toi l'a-
joy and you're our life too; To you be

- mour et le grand hon - neur!
hon - our and love dis - played.

CANADA

O CANADA

Words by
Sir Adolphe Basile Routhier (1839-1920)
English version by
R. STANLEY WEIR (1856-1926)

Music by
C. LAVALLÉE (1843-1891)
Arr. by H. A. CHAMBERS

1. O Ca - na - da! Ter -
2. *Sous l'œil de Dieu, près*
1. O Can - a - da! Our
2. O Can - a - da! Where

- re de nos aï - eux, Ton front est ceint de
du fleu - ve gé - ant, *Le* *Ca - na - dien* *gran -*
home and na - tive land! True pa - troit - love in
pines and ma - ples grow, Great prair - ies spread and

68

(CHORUS, S.A.T.B. *ad lib.* in English)

Et   ta   va - leur,   de   foi   trem - pé -   e,
Tou - jours gui - dé   par   sa   lu - miè -   re,
O   Can - a - da!   Glo - rious   and   free!___

O___   Can - a - da!___

Pro - té - ge - ra   nos   foy - ers   et   nos   droits,
Il   gar - de - ra   l'hon - neur   de   son   dra - peau,
We   stand   on   guard,   We   stand   on   guard   for   thee,

Pro - té - ge - ra nos foy - ers et nos ___ droits.
Il gar - de - ra l'hon - neur de son dra ___ peau.
O Can - a - da! We stand on guard for ___ thee.

3. *De son patron, précurseur du vrai Dieu,*
   Il porte au front l'auréole de feu.
   Ennemi de la tyrannie Mais plein de loyauté,
   Il veut garder dans l'harmonie, Sa fière liberté;
   Et par l'effort de son génie, Sur notre sol asseoir la vérité,
   Sur notre sol asseoir la vérité.

4. *Amour sacré du trône et de l'autel,*
   Remplis nos coeurs de ton souffle immortel!
   Parmi les races étrangères, Notre guide est la loi:
   Sachons être un peuple de frères, Sous le joug de la foi.
   Et répétons, comme nos pères, Le cri vainqueur: "Pour le Christ et le roi,"
   Le cri vainqueur: "Pour le Christ et le roi."

3. O Canada! Beneath thy shining skies
   May stalwart sons and gentle maidens rise
   To keep thee steadfast thro' the years
   From East to Western sea,
   Our own beloved native land,
   Our True North strong and free!

4. Ruler supreme, Who hearest humble pray'r,
   Hold our Dominion in Thy loving care.
   Help us to find, O God, in Thee
   A lasting rich reward,
   As waiting for the better day,
   We ever stand on guard.

CENTRAL AFRICAN REPUBLIC
La Renaissance

Words by BARTHÉLEMY BOGANDA   Music by HERBERT PEPPER

Alla Marcia moderato

O Cen - tra-fri - que, ô berceau des Bantous!

Re - prends ton droit au res - pect, à la vie!

Long - temps sou - mis, long - temps bri - mé par tous,

Mais de ce jour bri - sant la ty - ran - nie.

This National Anthem was adopted by the National Assembly on 25th May 1960.
The words are by the first President of the Central African Republic.

Dans le tra - vail, l'ordre et la di - gni - té,

Tu re - con - quiers ton droit, ton u - ni - té,

Et pour fran - chir cette é - ta - pe nou - vel - le,

Ped.　　　　　Ped.

De nos an - cê - tres la voix___ nous ap - pel - le.

Ped.　　　　　Ped.

CHORUS

Au tra-vail dans l'ordre et la di-gni-té, Dans le res-pect du

(Xylophones)

droit dans l'u-ni-té, Bri-sant la mi-sè-re et la ty-ran-nie,

Brandissant l'é-ten-dard _____ de la Pa-trie. _____

Translation by
T.M. CARTLEDGE

Oh! Central Africa, cradle of the Bantu!
Take up again your right to respect, to life!
Long subjugated, long scorned by all,
But, from today, breaking tyranny's hold.
Through work, order and dignity
You reconquer your rights, your unity,
And to take this new step
The voice of our ancestors calls us.

Chorus

To work! In order and dignity,
In the respect for rights and in unity,
Breaking poverty and tyranny,
Holding high the flag of the Fatherland.

E

CEYLON
Namō Namō Mathā

Words and melody by
ANANDA SAMARAKOON
Arr. by SURYA SENA

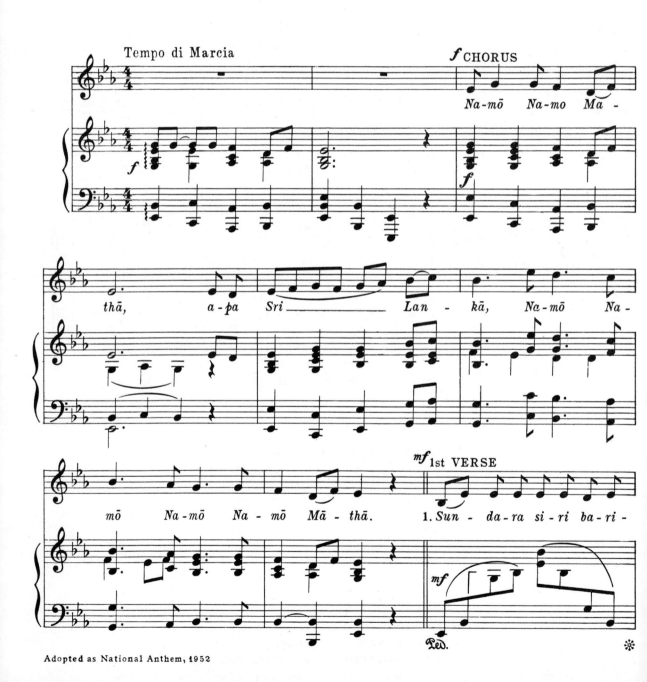

Tempo di Marcia

f CHORUS

Na-mō Na-mo Ma-thā, a-pa Sri _____ Lan-kā, Na-mō Na-mō Na-mō Na-mō Na-mō Mā-thā.

mf 1st VERSE

1. Sun-da-ra si-ri ba-ri-

Adopted as National Anthem, 1952

ni, Su-rän-di a - thi So - ba-mā - na Lan - ka

Ped.　　　✳ Ped.　　　✳ Ped.　　　✳

Dhan - ya dhan-a-ya ne - ka mal pa - la thu - ru pi - ri,

ja-ya bhoom - i - ya ram - yā.　A - pa ha-ta sä-pa si - ri

se-tha sad-a - nā,　jee - va-na-yē Ma - thā!

Pi-li-ga-nu ma-na a-pa bhak-ti poo-ja, Na-mō Na-mō Mā-

thā.   A-pa Sri _____ Lan-kā,   Na-mō   Na-

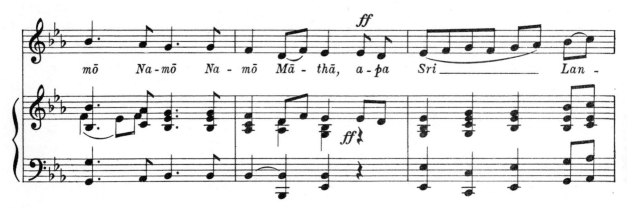

mō   Na-mō   Na-mō   Mā-thā,   a-pa Sri _____ Lan-

kā,   Na-mō   Na-mō   Na-mō   Na-mō   Mā-thā. _____

2. *Obave apa vidya obamaya apa sathya*
   ..... obave apa shakti
   apa hada thula bhakti oba apa āloke
   apage anuprane oba apa jeevana ve
   apa muktiya obave

3. *Nava jēevana demine nithina apa*
   pubudu karan māthā
   Gnana vēerya vadavamina ragena yanu
   mana jaya bhōomi karā
   Eka mavekuge daru kala bavinā
   yamu yamu wee nopamā
   Prema vadamu sama bheda durara
             Namō Namō Māthā

Free Translation by Dr. C.W.W. Kannangara

Mother Lanka – we worship Thee!
Plenteous in prosperity, Thou,
Beauteous in grace and love,
Laden with corn and luscious fruit
And fragrant flowers of radiant hue,
Giver of life and all good things,
Our land of joy and victory,
Receive our grateful praise sublime,
Lanka! we worship Thee.

Thou gavest us Knowledge and Truth,
Thou art our strength and inward faith,
Our light divine and sentient being,
Breath of life and liberation.
Grant us, bondage free, inspiration.
Inspire us for ever.
In wisdom and strength renewed,
Ill-will, hatred, strife all ended,
In love enfolded, a mighty nation
Marching onward, all as one,
Lead us, Mother, to fullest freedom.

CHAD
La Tchadienne

Words by
Father GIDROL, S.J. and
students of St. Paul's School★

Music by
Father VILLARD, A.J.,
Arr. by Col. P. DUPONT

Peu - ple Tcha-dien, de - bout et à l'ou-vra - ge! Tu as con-

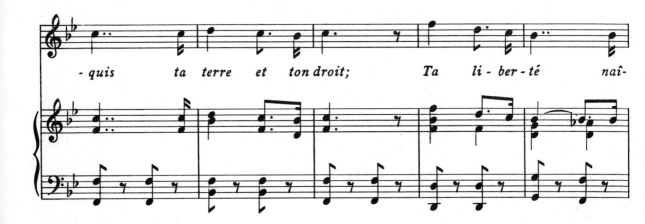

-quis ta terre et ton droit; Ta li - ber - té naî-

★St. Paul's School at Fort Archambault trains
teachers for Catholic education in Chad.

-tra de ton cou-ra-ge. Lè - ve les yeux, l'a-ve-nir est à Toi.

O mon Pa - ys,

que Dieu te prenne en gar - - de,

Que tes voi - sins ad - mi - rent tes en-fants. Jo-

yeux, pa - ci - fique, a - vance en - chan - tant, Fi - dèle à tes an -

ciens qui te re - gar - - - dent.

English Translation
by T.M.Cartledge

CHORUS

People of Chad, arise and take up the task!
You have conquered the soil and your rights;
Your freedom will be born of your courage.
Lift up your eyes, the future is yours.

VERSE

Oh, my Country, may God protect you,
May your neighbours admire your children.
Joyful, peaceful, advance as you sing,
Faithful to your fathers who are watching you.

Repeat Chorus

CHILE

Words by
EUSEBIO LILLO (1826-1910)

Music by
RAMÓN CARNICER
(1789-1855)

Marziale

The original words of this National Anthem were written in 1819.   In 1847 when a new Peace
Treaty was signed between Chile and Spain, the Chilean government requested Eusebio Lillo
to write new words, without bitterness towards Spain, the 'mother country'.

Chi - le es tu cie - lo a - zu - la - do pu - ras
Chi - le, thy skies spread a - bove thee, So

bri - sas te cru - zan tam - bién, y tu
sweet are the breez - es that roam O'er thy

cam - po de flo - res bor - da - do es la
fields rich - ly broi - dered with flow - er - lets That

co - pia fe - liz del E - dén. Ma - ges-
an - gels might make thee their home! Grand - ly

-me - te fu-tu - ro_es - plen - dor._____ y__ e - se
fu - ture_____ whis - pers its word._____ And____ the____

mar___ que tranqui - lo__ te ba - ña te____ pro -
sea____ like a tran - quil_____ foun - tain Of___ thy__

-me - te___ fu-tu - ro es - plen - dor.
fu - ture____ whis - pers its word.

CHORUS

Dul - - - ce Pa - - - tria, re -
Dear_____ Home - - - land ac -

- ci - - be___ los___ vo - tos
- cept_____ the___ vows___

con que Chi - - le en tus
On thine al - - tars that

a - - ras___ ju - ró que o la
Chi - - le___ shall___ be A___

tum - ba se - rá de los li - bres o el a -
re - fuge from for - eign op - pres - sion Or the

CHINA
(Nationalist)

Words based on a speech by
Dr. SUN YAT SEN (1867-1925)
Translated by
TU T'ING-HSIU

Music by
CHE'NG MAO-YÜN (1928)
Arr. by
Professor HUANG CHIH

Adopted as the National Anthem in 1929
The words 'San Min Chu I' express Dr. Sun's political philosophy
of the Three People's Principles, i.e. government of the people, by
the people, and for the people.

yeh fei shieh, chu I shih tsung, shih ching shih __
fast your aim, by sun and star, Be earn - est and

yung, pi shing pi ___ chung, I
brave, your coun - try to save, One

hsin I ___ teh, kuan cheh shih ___ chung!
heart, one ___ soul, one mind one ___ goal!

F

CHINA
Communist

Words by T'IEN HAN

Music by NIE ERH

This song was written in 1932. On the 27th September 1949 it
was officially approved as the National Anthem of Communist China.
Reproduced from Die National-Hymnen der Erde by permission of
the publisher, Max Hueber Verlag.

Unofficial Translation

Rise! We do not want to be slaves,
Build anew the long wall from flesh and blood,
For China's people is in greatest danger
And the oppressed cry loud from fury.
Oh rise, oh rise, oh rise,
Millions we are, and yet but one in heart,
For we throw ourselves with courage on the enemy,
Forward,
For we throw ourselves with courage on the enemy,
Forward, forward, forward!

COLOMBIA

Words by
RAFAEL NUÑEZ
(1825-1894)

Music by
ORESTES SÍNDICI

This anthem was sung for the first time c. 1905. Rafael Nuñez was elected
President of Colombia four times.

sur - cos de do - lo - res El bien ger - mi - na__

ya, El__ bien ger - mi - na__ ya. ¡Oh glo - ria in-mar-ce -

- si - ble! ¡Oh jú - bi-lo in-mor-tal! En__

sur - cos_ de do - lo-res El__ bien ger - mi - na ya.

VERSE

1. Ce - só la ho-rri - ble __ no - che, La li - ber-tad __ su -

- bli - me De - rra - ma las __ au - ro - ras

De su in-ven-ci - ble luz. La hu - ma - ni-dad en -

- te - ra, Que en - tre ca - de - nas gi - me, Com -

-pren - de las pa-la - bras Del que murió en la Cruz.

2. *INDEPENDENCIA grita*
    El mundo americano;
    Se baña en sangre de héroes
    La tierra de Colón.
    Pero este gran principio:
    EL REY NO ES SOBERANO,
    Resuena, y los que sufren
    Bendicen su pasión.

CHORUS

Oh unfading glory!
Oh immortal joy!
In furrows of pain
Good is already germinating.

1. The fearful night came to an end,
    Liberty sublime
    Is spreading the dawns
    Of its invincible light.
    The whole of humanity,
    Which is groaning under chains,
    Understands the words
    Of the One who died on the Cross.

2. INDEPENDENCE cries
    The American world;
    In heroes' blood is bathing
    The Land of Columbus.
    But this great principle:
    THE KING IS NOT SOVEREIGN,
    Resounds, and those who suffer
    Praise the passion in it.

CONGO (Brazzaville)
La Congolaise

Words and Melody by
JEAN ROYER
JACQUES TONDRA
JO SPADILIERE

Arr. by HENRY COLEMAN

Maestoso

1. En ce jour le so-leil se lè - ve Et no-
2. Des fo - rêts jus-qu'à la sa-va - ne, Des sa-

-tre Con - go res - plen - dit. U - ne lon - gue nuit s'a -
-va - nes jus-qu'à la mer, Un seul peuple, u - ne seule

-chè - ve, Un grand bon - heur a sur - gi. Chan-tons
â - me, Un seul cœur, ar - dent et fier. Lut-tons

tous a - vec i - vres - se le chant de la li - ber - té.
tous, tant que nous som - mes, pour no-tre vieux pa - ys noir.

Con - go-lais, de - bout fiè - re-ment par - tout, Pro-cla-mons l'u - nion de no-

-tre na - tion, Ou-bli - ons ce qui nous di - vi - se, so-yons

plus u - nis que ja - mais, Vi-vons pour no - tre de-

-vi - se: U - ni - té, tra - vail, pro - grès! Vi-vons

pour no-tre de-vi - se: U-ni-té, tra-vail, pro-grès!

3. *Et s'il nous faut mourir, en somme*
   Qu'importe puisque nos enfants,
   Partout, pourront dire comme
   On triomphe en combattant,
   Et dans le moindre village
   Chantent sous nos trois couleurs.

Translation by T. M. Cartledge

1. On this day the sun rises
   And our Congo stands resplendent.
   A long night is ended,
   A great happiness has come.
   Let us all, with wild joyfulness, sing
   The song of freedom.

CHORUS Arise, Congolese, proud every man,
   Proclaim the unity of our nation.
   Let us forget what divides us
   And become more united than ever.
   Let us live our motto:
   Unity, work, progress.
   Let us live our motto:
   Unity, work, progress.

2. From the forest to the bush,
   From the bush to the ocean,
   One people, one soul,
   One heart, ardent and proud.
   Let us all fight, every one of us,
   For our old black country.

3. And if we have to die,
   What does it really matter? Our children
   Everywhere will be able to say how
   Triumph comes through battle,
   And in the smallest village
   Sing beneath our three colours.

CONGO

(Kinshasa)

Debout Kongolais

(Song of Independence)

Words and Music by
J. LUTUMBA and S. BOKA
Piano arrangement by T. M. Cartledge

De - bout Kon - go-lais, U - nis par le sort, U - nis dans l'ef-fort pour l'in - dé - pen - dan - ce, Dres - sons nos fronts _____ long - temps cour -

This National Song was written to celebrate Independence, attained on 30 June 1960.

-bés _____ Et pour de bon pre - nons le plus bel é -

- lan, dans la paix, O peuple ar - dent, _____ par le la -

- beur, _____ nous bâ - ti - rons un pa - ys plus beau qu'a - vant, dans la paix.

Ci - toy - ens, en - ton - nez _____ l'hym - ne sa - cré de vo - tre so - li - da - ri - té, Fiè - re - ment, sa - lu - ez _____ l'em - blè - me d'or de vo - tre sou - ve - rai - ne - té, Kon - go.

(REFRAIN)

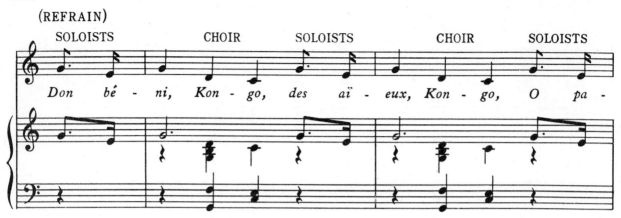

Don bé - ni, Kon - go, des aï - eux, Kon - go, O pa -

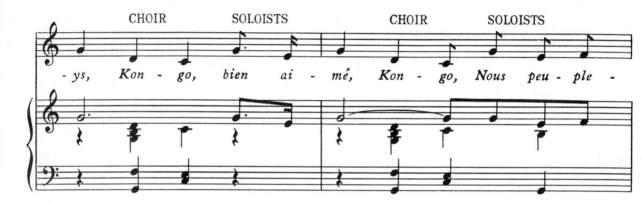

- ys, Kon - go, bien ai - mé, Kon - go, Nous peu - ple -

- rons ton sol et nous as - su - re - rons ta gran - deur. Tren - te

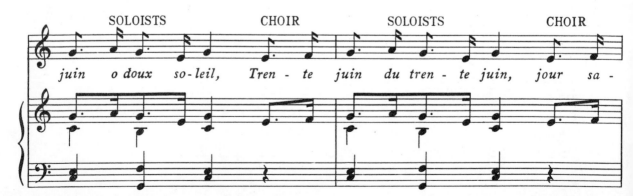

juin o doux so - leil, Tren - te juin du tren - te juin, jour sa -

cré, sois le té-moin, jour sa - cré, de l'im-mor-tel ser-ment de li - ber-té

Que nous lé-guons à no - tre pos-té- ri- té pour tou - jours.

English Translation
by T. M. Cartledge

CHOIR   Arise, Congolese, united by fate,
United in the struggle for independence,
Let us hold up our heads, so long bowed,
And now, for good, let us keep moving boldly ahead, in peace.
Oh, ardent people, by hard work we shall build,
In peace, a country more beautiful than before.

VERSE   Countrymen, sing the sacred hymn of your solidarity,
Proudly salute the golden emblem of your sovereignty, Congo.

REFRAIN   Blessed gift (Congo) of our forefathers (Congo),
Oh (Congo) beloved country (Congo),
We shall people your soil and ensure your greatness.
(30th June) Oh gentle sun (30th June) of 30th June,
(Sacred day) Be witness (sacred day) of the immortal oath of freedom
That we hand on to our children for ever.

(In the part marked "Refrain" the words in brackets are marked for singing
by Choir, the rest being marked for singing by "Soloists".)

COSTA RICA

Words by
JOSÉ MARIA ZELEDÓN (b.1877)
(adopted in 1900)
English verses by
MARY ELIZABETH and DICCON SHAW

Music by
MANUEL MARÍA GUTIÉRREZ
(1829-1887)

Allegro Marcial

Noble patria tu hermo-sa ban-de-ra   ex-pre-
No-ble coun-try, the life of your peo-ple Is re-

-sión de tu vi-da nos da: ba-jo el lím-pi-do a-zul de tu
-veal'd in the flag that you fly;   For in peace, white and pure, they live

Adopted as the National Anthem in 1853, when composed.
The first two verses allude to the national flag, of
which the colours are blue, white and red.
English words copyright J. B. Cramer & Co. Ltd.

cie - lo blan-ca y pu - ra des-can - sa la paz.
tran - quil 'Neath the clear lim-pid blue of your sky.

En la lu - cha te - naz de fe-cun - da la - bor que en-ro-
And their fa - ces are rud-dy with ar - du - ous toil In the

- je - ce del hom - bre la faz, con-qui - sta - ron tus
fields 'neath the life - giv - ing sun. Though your sons are but

hi - jos— la-brie-gos sen-ci - llos— e-ter - no pres-ti - gio, es-ti - ma y ho-
pea - sants, their la - bours e - ter - nal Es-teem,— re - nown,— and hon - our have

G

-nor e - ter - no pres - ti - gio, es - ti - ma y ho - nor.
won, es - teem,__ re - nown,__ and hon - our have won.

¡Sal-ve, oh tie - rra gen-til! ¡Sal-ve, oh ma - dre de a -
Hail, oh land of our birth! gra-cious land that we

- mor! Cuan-do al - gu - no pre - ten - da tu glo - ria man -
love! If an en - e - my seek - ing to slan - der you,

- char,__ ve - rás a tu pue - blo, va - lien - te y vi -
harms__ Your name, then__ we will a - ban - don our

-ril, la__ tos-ca he-rra-mien - ta en ar - ma tro -
farms And a-rise__ with fer - vour to take__ up our

ff

-car. ¡Sal-ve, oh pa-tria! tu pró - di - go sue - lo dul - ce a-
arms. O sweet coun - try, our re - fuge and shel - ter; How__

-bri - go y sus-ten - to nos da; ba-jo el lím - pi-do a-zul de tu
fer - tile your life - giv - ing soil! May your peo - ple, con-tent - ed and

cie - lo ¡vi - van siem pre el tra-ba - jo y la paz!
peace - ful, Un - mo - lest - ed con - tin - ue their toil.

rall.

CUBA

La Bayamesa

Translated by
G. H. HATCHMAN

Versified by
MARTIN SHAW

Words and Music by
PEDRO FIGUEREDO
(1819-1870)

Al com-ba-te co-rred, ba-ya-
Swift, oh men of Ba-ya-mo, to

Sung for the first time in 1868 during the battle of Bayamo,
in which Figueredo played a leading part.

By permission of J.B.Cramer & Co.Ltd.

-de - nas vi - vir, es vi - vir_____ en a-
-mit to the bon - dage of a - - - liens Is to

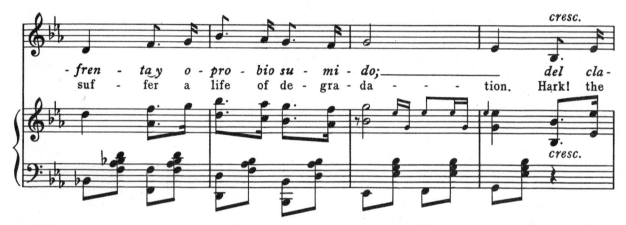

cresc.

-fren - ta y o - pro - bio su - mi - do;_____ del cla-
suf - fer a life of de - gra - - - tion. Hark! the

cresc.

-rín es - cu - chad el so - ni - - - do; ¡a las
trum - pet is call - ing your na - - - tion! Va - liant

ar - mas, va-lien - tes, co - rred!_____ En ca-
he - roes, "To arms!" be your cry._____ To sub-

pp

pp

CZECHOSLOVAKIA

Part 1: Kde Domov Můj?

Words by
JOSEF KAJETÁN TYL
(1808-1856)

Music by
FRANTIŠEK SAN ŠKROUP,
(1801-1862)

This State hymn was officially recognised as the National Anthem in 1919.
It is in two parts. The first is Czech and the second is a Slovak folksong
commemorating the exodus of Slovak students from Bratislavia in 1843.

ráj____ to na po-hled! A to je ta krá - sná ze - mě, ze-mě

če - ská do-mov můj, ___ ze-mě če - ská do-mov můj!

Part 2: Nad Tatrú sa blýská

Words by
JANKO MATÚSKA

Traditional Melody

Allegro energico

Nad Ta - trú sa blý - ská, hro - my di - vo bi - jú,

nad Ta - trú sa blý - ská, hro - my di - vo bi - jú.

Part 1

Where is my home, where is my home?
Streams are rushing through the meadows,
'Mid the rocks sigh fragrant pine groves,
Orchards decked in Spring's array
Scenes of Paradise portray.
And this land of wond'rous beauty
Is the Czech land, home of mine
Is the Czech land, home of mine

Part 2

Lightning strikes our mighty Tatra tempest-shaken,
Lightning strikes our mighty Tatra tempest-shaken.
Stand we fast, friends of mine,
Storms must pass, sun will shine,
Slovaks shall awaken.

DAHOMEY

L'Aube Nouvelle

THE DAWN OF A NEW DAY

Words and music by the
Abbé G. DAGNON
Arr. by HENRY COLEMAN

Con spirito

1. Ja - dis à son ap- -pel, nos aï - eux sans fai - bles - se Ont su a- -vec cou - rage, ar - deur, pleins d'al - lé - gres - se Li-

Adopted as the National Anthem at the declaration of independence, August, 1960

CHORUS

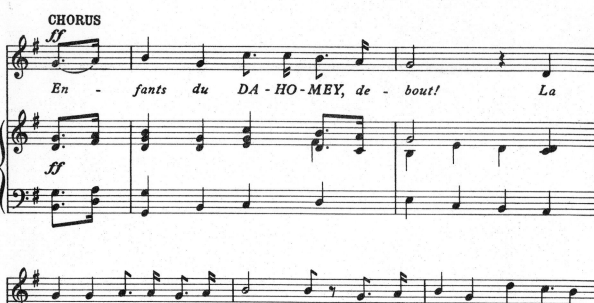

En - fants du DA - HO - MEY, de - bout! La

li - ber - té d'un cri so - no - re Chante aux pre-miers feux de l'au-

-ro - re; En - fants du DA - HO - MEY, de - bout!

2. *Quand partout souffle un vent de colère et de haine,*
Dahoméen, sois fier, et d'une âme sereine,
Confiant dans l'avenir, regarde ton drapeau!
Dans le vert tu liras l'espoir du renouveau,
De tes aïeux le rouge évoque le courage;
Des plus riches trésors le jaune est le présage.

3. *Tes monts ensoleillés, tes palmiers, ta verdure,*
   Cher DAHOMEY, partout font ta vive parure.
   Ton sol offre à chacun la richesse des fruits.
   DAHOMEY, désormais que tes fils tous unis
   D'un fraternel élan partagent l'espérance
   De te voir à jamais heureux dans l'abondance.

English Paraphrase by
ELIZABETH P. COLEMAN

Chorus

Children of Dahomey, arise!
The resounding cry of freedom
Is heard at the first light of dawn;
Children of Dahomey, arise!

1. Formerly, at her call, our ancestors
   Knew how to engage in mighty battles
   With strength, courage, ardour, and full of joy, but at the price of blood.
   Builders of the present, you too, join forces
   Each day for the task stronger in unity
   Build without ceasing for posterity.

2. When all around there blows a wind of anger and hate:
   Citizen of Dahomey be proud, and in a calm spirit
   Trusting in the future, behold your flag!
   In the green you read hope of spring;
   The red signifies the courage of your ancestors;
   The yellow foretells the richest treasures.

3. Beloved Dahomey, your sunny mountains, palm trees, and green pastures
   Show everywhere your brightness;
   Your soil offers everyone the richest fruits.
   Dahomey, from henceforth your sons are united
   With one brotherly spirit sharing the hope of seeing you
   Enjoy abundance and happiness for ever.

DENMARK
Kong Kristian

Words by
JOHANNES EWALD (1743-1781)
English versification by
H.W. LONGFELLOW
(1807-1882)

Music by
D.L. ROGERT (?)
(1742-1813)
This is not certain.

Maestoso

Kong Kri-stian stod ved høj - en Mast i røg og
King Christ -ian stood by the loft - y mast In mist and

damp. Hans vær - ge ham-re - de så fast, at
smoke; His sword was ham - mer - ing so fast, Through

go - tens hjælm og hjer - ne brast; da sank hver fjendt - ligt
Go - thic helm and brain it passed; Then sank each hos - tile

This is the official National and Royal Anthem. Music first appeared in ms. form c.1762-1777;
words first used in the ballad opera *The Fishermen* 1780. There are other verses.
★ King Christian IV (1577-1648) was one of Denmark's great patriotic leaders.

spejl og _ mast i røg og damp. "Fly," skreg de, "fly, hvad
hulk and mast In mist and smoke. "Fly!" shout-ed they, "fly,

flyg - te kan! Hvo står for Dan - marks Kri - sti - an, hvo
he who can! Who braves of Den - mark's Christ - i - an, Who

står for Dan - marks Kri - sti - an i kamp?"
braves of Den - mark's Christ-i - an The stroke?"

DENMARK

Der er et yndigt land

Words by
ADAM GOTTLOB OEHLENSCHLÄGER(1779-1850)
Translated by
CHARLES BRATLI

Music by
HANS ERNST KRØYER
(1798-1879)

Der er et yn - digt land, det
I know a love - ly land, Whose

står med bre - de bø - ge naer sal - ten ø - ster-
charm - ing woods of beech - es Grow near the Bal - tic

- strand, naer sal - ten ø - ster - strand;
strand, Grow near the Bal - tic strand.

Also used on national occasions. Written c. 1819. Its popularity as a national song
dates from 4th July, 1844, when students sang it at a national festal meeting to a
gathering of 12,000 Danes.

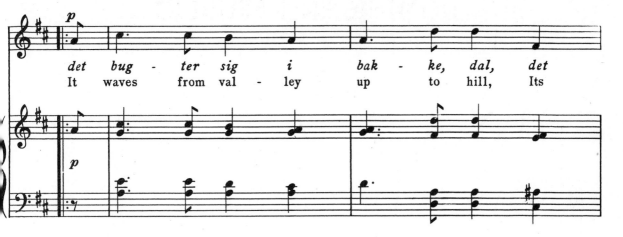

det bug - ter sig i bak - ke, dal, det
It waves from val - ley up to hill, Its

cresc.   f   p

hed - der gam - le Dan - mark, og det er Frej - as
name is old - en Den - mark, And here dwells Frey - a

sal,___ og det er Frej - - as sal.
still,___ And here dwells Frey - - a still.

DOMINICAN REPUBLIC

Words by
EMILIO PRUD'HOMME
English versification by
J.E. HALES and
MARY ELIZABETH SHAW

Music by
JOSÉ REYES (1835-1905)

Quis-que-ya - nos va-lien - tes, al -
Va - liant sons of Quis-que - ya, our

-ce - mos nues-tro can - to_ con vi - va e - mo - ción, Y_ del
chor - us, Let us, heart-felt_ and strong, sing to the world; While, de-

First sung as National Anthem in 1900. Quisqueya is the native name of the island of Santo Domingo.
By permission of J.B. Cramer & Co. Ltd.

mun - do a la faz os - ten - te - mos nues-tro in - vic - to glo - rio - so pen -
-fi - ant and daunt - less, be - fore us We will flou - rish our stan - dard un -

-dón. ¡Sal - ve el pue - blo que in tré - pi - do y fuer - te, a la
furled. Hail! O peo - ple in - tre - pid and dar - ing, Who with

gue - rra a mo - rir se lan - zó. Cuan-do en bé - li - co re - to de
ea - ger - ness sprang to at - tack; And, of blood-shed and dan - ger un -

muer - te sus ca - de - nas de es - cla - vo rom -
-car - ing, Saw the fet - ters of sla - ve - ry

-pió.
crack.

Nin-gun pue - blo ser li - bre me -
Un - de - serv - ing of free - dom the

-re - ce si es es - cla - vo in do - len - te y ser - vil: Si en su
na - tion Which in ty - ran - ny's bond tame - ly lives, And is

pe - cho la lla - ma no cre - ce que tem -
lack - ing the fine in - spi - ra - tion That from

-pló_el he-ro-is-mo vi-ril. Mas Quis-que-ya la_in-dó-mi-ta_y
true vi-rile cour-age de-rives. But_ the sons of Quis-que-ya ne'er

bra - - va Siem-pre_al-ti - va la fren-te_al-za-
fail her, And her head car-ried high shall re-

-rá: Que si fue - re mil ve - ces es -
-main; Though a thou-sand times foes should as -

-cla - va Ó-tras tan-tas ser li - bre sa - brá.
-sail her, She her free-dom would e - ver re - gain.

ECUADOR

Words by
JUAN LEÓN MERA
(1832-1894)
English versification by
T. M. CARTLEDGE

Music by
ANTONIO NEUMANE
(1818-1871)

Officially recognized as the National Anthem by a government decree in 1948.
It had been in use for a considerable time before. The author, in his later years, was President of the Senate of Ecuador.

ró y a -cep-tó el ho - lo - ca - us - to Ye - sa,
on and ac-cept - ed the sa - cri-fice, And that

san - gre fue ger-men fe-cun - do De o -tros
blood was seed pro - li - fic; Oth - er

hé - roes que a - tó - ni -to el mun - do Vió en tu
her - oes the world ob-served, as -tound - ed, For the

tor - no a mi - lla - res sur - gir.
fight rise___ up - on ev - 'ry hand.

Dios mi -
God look'd

-gir.
hand.

a mi - lla - res sur -
rise___ up - on ev - 'ry

-gir,
hand.

a mi - lla - res sur - gir.
rise up - on ev - 'ry hand.

D.% al Fine

ÉIRE (IRELAND)
Amhrán na bhFiann
THE SOLDIER'S SONG

Words by
PEADAR KEARNEY (c.1909)

Music by
PEADAR KEARNEY and PATRICK HEANEY
Arr. by T. M. CARTLEDGE

Tempo di Marcia — VERSE

1. *Seo dhibh, a — cháir - de du-an Óg-láigh, Cath-*
1. We'll sing a — song, a sol - dier's song, With

-réim - each briogh-mhar ceol — mhar, Ár dtein - te — cnámh go
cheer - ing, rous - ing cho - rus, As round our — blaz - ing

bu - a - cach táid, 'San spéir go mín réal - tó - gach, Is
fires we — throng, The star - ry heav - ens o'er us; Im -

By permission of Minister of Finance, Éire.
Chorus adopted as Irish National Anthem, July 1926

fonn - mhar faobh - rach sinn chun gleo, 'S go tiún - mhar glé roimh
-pa - tient for the com - ing fight, And as we wait the

thiocht do'n ló, Fé chiú - nas chaomh na hoi - che ar seol: Seo libh,
morn - ing's light, Here in the si - lence of the night, We'll

can - aidh Amh-rán na bhFiann.
chant a sol - dier's song.

CHORUS

Sinn - ne Fian - na Fáil A-
Sol - diers are we, Whose

-tá fé gheall ag Éir - inn, Buidhean dár sluagh Thar
lives are pledged to Ire - land; Some have come From a

lámhach   na — bpiléar,   Seo libh,   can-aidh   Amh-rán   na bhFiann.
ri - fles'— peal   We'll   chant   a   sol - dier's song.

2. *Cois bánta réidhe, ar árdaibh sléibhe,*
   Ba bhuadhach ár sinnsear romhainn,
   Ag lámhach go tréan fé'n sár-bhrat séin
   Tá thuas sa ghaoith go seolta.
   Ba dhúthchas riamh d'ár gcine cháidh
   Gan iompáil siar ó imirt áir,
   'S ag siubhal mar iad i gcoinnibh námhad
   Seo libh, canaidh Amhrán na bhFiann.

   CURFÁ: Sinn-ne Fianna Fáil, etc.

3. *A bhuidhean nách fann d'fhuil Ghaoidheal is Gall,*
   Sin breacadh lae na saoirse,
   Tá sgeimhle 's sgannradh i gcroidhthibh namhad,
   Roimh ranngaibh laochra ár dtíre.
   Ár dteinte is tréith gan spréach anois,
   Sin luisne ghlé san spéir anoir,
   'S an biodhbha i raon na bpiléar agaibh:
   Seo libh, canaidh Amhrán na bhFiann.

   CURFÁ: Sinn-ne Fianna Fáil, etc.

2. In valley green, on towering crag,
   Our fathers fought before us,
   And conquered 'neath the same old flag
   That's proudly floating o'er us.
   We're children of a fighting race,
   That never yet has known disgrace,
   And as we march, the foe to face,
   We'll chant a soldier's song.

   CHORUS: Soldiers are we, etc.

3. Sons of the Gael! Men of the Pale!
   The long watched day is breaking;
   The serried ranks of Inisfail
   Shall set the Tyrant quaking.
   Our camp fires now are burning low:
   See in the east a silv'ry glow,
   Out yonder waits the Saxon foe,
   So chant a soldier's song.

   CHORUS: Soldiers are we, etc.

EL SALVADOR

Words by
JUAN J. CAÑAS (1826-1912)
English versification by
MARY ELIZABETH
AND DICCON SHAW

Music by
JUAN ABERLE

Andante maestoso

CHORUS *mf solenne*

Sa - lu -
Moth - er

- de - mos la Pa - tria or - gu - llo - sos De hi - jos
coun - try, thy peo - ple sa - lute thee! Proud - ly the

This was written in 1879 and adopted as the National Anthem in 1953
General Juan Cañas was a diplomat and soldier; at one time Minister of Foreign Affairs.

su - yos po-der - nos lla - mar_____ Y ju-
name_____ of thy chil - dren we bear,_____ And with

- re - mos la vi - da a - ni - mo - sos Sin des-
bold and un-tir - ing de - vo - tion To thy_____

can - so a su bien con - sa - grar.
ser - vice our lives let us swear.

Sa - lu -
Moth - er

-de - mos la Pa - tria or - gu - llo - sos De hi - jos
coun - try, thy peo - ple sa - lute thee! Proud - ly the

su - llos po - der - nos lla - mar____ Y ju -
name__ of thy chil - dren we bear,____ And with

- re - mos la vi - da a - ni - mo - sos Sin des -
bold and un - tir - ing de - vo - tion to thy____

- can - so a su bien____ con - sa - grar
ser - vice our lives____ let us swear.

con - sa - grar
Our lives we swear,

con - sa - grar
Our lives we swear,

con - sa -
Our lives we

- grar
swear,

con - sa - grar
Our lives we swear.

Fine **p** VERSE

1. *De la* paz en la di-cha su -
1. Peace, con - tent - ment, and hap-pi-ness

Fine

-pre - - ma Siem-pre no - ble___ so-ñó El Sal-va dor___ Fué ob-te-
ev - - er Was the con-stant dream___ of El___ Sal - va - dor; To a-

-ner - - la su e-ter-no pro-ble - - - ma, Con - ser-
-chieve it was her glor-ious am - bi - - - tion, And to

-var - la es su glo - - - ria ma - yor. Y con
keep___ it for ev - - - - er - more. For with

fé in-que - bran-ta - ble el ca - mi - no___ Del pro-
ea - ger faith which nev - - er shall fal - ter___ Towards the

-gre - so se a-fa - na en se-guir en se-guir Por lle-
bright star of pro - gress she fol - lows the way; To se-

-nar—— su gran-dio - so des - ti - no,——— Con quis-
-cure—— for her-self a hap - py fu - ture,——— And her

-tar—— se un fe - liz—— por-ve - nir Le pro-
des - ti - ny glo - rious o - bey. The at-

-te——— je u-na fè-rrea ba - rre - ra Con tra el
-tack——— of a vil - lain - ours trai - tor Her——

CORO   *Saludemos la patria orgullosos*
De Hijos suyos podernos llamar;
Y juremos la vida animosos,
Sin descanso a su bien consagrar.

2.   *Libertad es su dogma, es su guia,*
Que mil veces logró defender;
Y otras tantas de audaz tirania
Rechazar el odioso poder.
Dolorosa y sangrienta es su historia,
Pero excelsa y brillante a la vez,
Manantial de legitima gloria,
Gran lección de espartana altivez.
No desmaya su innata bravura:
En cada hombre hay un héroe inmortal,
Que sabrá mantenerse a la altura
De su antiguo valor proverbial.

3.   *Todos son abnegados y fieles*
Al prestigio del bélico ardor,
Con que siempre segaron laureles
De la Patria salvando el honor.
Respetar los derechos extraños
Y apoyarse en la recta razón
Es para ella, sin torpes amaños,
La invariable, más firme ambición.
Y en seguir esta linea se aferra,
Dedicando su esfuerzo tenaz
En hacer cruda guerra a la guerra;
Su ventura se encuentra en la paz.

CHORUS   Mother country, thy people salute thee!
Proudly the name of thy children we bear,
And with bold and untiring devotion
To thy service our lives let us swear.

2.   Never tiring, her people have battled
To preserve and guard their liberty:
And with valour have a thousand times over
Broken the powers of base tyranny.
For, though brilliant and sublime is her story,
Yet it tells of her blood and her suffering beside,
And in this is revealed her true glory
And her noble and stoical pride.
All her sons shall be heroes immortal;
They are daring, resourceful, and bold;
For their bravery is a tradition
And they fight like their fathers of old.

3.   They will follow this ancient tradition
Which has won for them undying fame
Since with ardour, self-denying and faithful,
They kept spotless their Motherland's name.
Her ambition is firm and unchanging,
To respect and observe others' rights is her pride;
To maintain ever pure the fount of justice
Where uprightness and trust are allied.
She will follow this path with devotion
And with courage which never shall cease;
For, although she gives battle for battle,
Her most fervent desire is for peace.

ESTONIA

Words by
JOHANN WOLDEMAR JANSSEN (1819-1900)

Music by
FREDRIK PACIUS (1809-1891)
Arr. by
HENRY COLEMAN

Maestoso con entusiasmo

Lyrics (beneath vocal line):

Mu i - sa - maa, mu õnn ja rõõm, Kui kau - nis o - led sa! Ei lei - a mi - na ii - al teal See suu - re lai - a il - ma peal, Mis mull' nii ar - mas o - leks ka Kui sa mu i - sa - maa!

First acknowledged as Estonia's National Anthem c.1917. Sung for first time at National Singing Festival, 1st July, 1869
The tune is the same as that of Finland's National Anthem.
The National Anthem of the U.S.S.R. is now used inside Estonia.

2. *Sa oled mind ju sünnitand*
   Ja üles kasvatand;
   Sind tänan mina alati
   Ja jään sul truuks surmani!
   Mul kõige armsam oled sa,
   Mu kallis isamaa!

3. *Su üle Jumal valvaku,*
   Mu armas isamaa!
   Ta olgu sinu kaitseja
   Ja võtku rohkest' õnnista'
   Mis iial ette võtad sa,
   Mu kallis isamaa!

Translation by Jenny Wahl

1. My native land, my joy, delight,
   How fair thou art and bright;
   And nowhere in the world all round
   Can ever such a place be found
   So well beloved as I love thee,
   My native country dear!

2. My little cradle stood on thy soil,
   Whose blessings ease my toil.
   With my last breath my thanks to thee,
   For true to death I'll ever be
   O worthy, most beloved and fine,
   Thou, dearest country mine!

3. May God in Heaven thee defend,
   My best, my dearest land!
   May He be guard, may He be shield,
   For ever may He bless and wield
   O graciously all deeds of thine,
   Thou dearest country mine!

ETHIOPIA

Words by a group of
ETHIOPIANS (1930)
English versification by
SEBASTIAN SHAW

Music by
K. NALBANDIAN
(1925)

Moderato

mf E - thi - o - pia hoy Dess yi - be - lish Be - am - la -
Hail E - thi - o - pia, land e - lect! The pow - er of

-kish hail Be - ne - goo___ sish f Te - ba - - be - re - wal___
God your King di - rect___ Your va - liant___ war - riors, in___

ar - beg - no - chish A - yin - ne - kam___ ket - to
un - ion se - lect, Their dear land's lib - er -

First performed at the coronation of Haile Selaisse I. 2nd November, 1930

ne - tsan - ne - tish. *Ber - too na - che -*
-ty to pro - tect. They from moun - tain

-wuna te - ra - ro - chish A - ti - fe - rim. Ke - te - la -
strong-holds shall ef - fect Your foes' down - fall; fear they re -

-to - chish Del ad - ra - gi - wu ne - goo - sa - chin
-ject. May our vic - tor - i - ous and great King

Yi - noo - rel - len le - keb - ra - chin.
Live for long and new glo - ry bring.

FAROE ISLANDS
Tú alfagra land mítt

Words by
SÍMUN av SKARÐI
English translation by
C. NISSEN

Music by
PETER ALBERG (1907)
Arr. by HENRY COLEMAN

1. Tú al - fagr - a land mítt, mín dýr - ast - a ogn! Á

vetr - i - so rand - hvítt, á sumr - i við logn, tú

tek - ur meg at tær, so tætt í tín favn. Tit

oyggj - ar so mæt - ar, Gud sign - i tað navn, sum

menn tykk - um gov - u, tá teir tykk - um só - u, Ja,

Gud sign - i Føroy - ar, mítt land!

2. *Hin roðin, sum skínur*
á sumri í líð;
hin óðnin, sum týnir
mangt lív vetrartíð,
og myrkrið, sum fjalir
mær bjartasta mál,
og ljósið, sum spælir
mær sigur í sál:
alt streingir, ið tóna,
sum vága og vóna,
at eg verji Føroyar, mítt land!

3. *Eg nígi ti niður*
í bøn til tín, Gud:
Hin heilagi friður
mær falli í lut!
Lat sál mína tváa
sær í tíni dýrd!
So torir hon vága,
– av Gudi væl skírd –
at bera tað merki,
sum eyðkennir verkið,
ið varðveitir Føroyar, mítt land!

Free Translation

1. Oh, Faroe Islands, my dearest treasure!
   When winter storms roar, in warm summer night,
   You draw out yonder my home in your embrace.
   You Islands so graceful, God bless the name
   That our forefathers gave you when beyond the ocean they found you.
   Yes, God bless the Faroe Islands, my land.

2. That sun gleam which hovers round summer green time
   And the storm which claims so many a life in winter;
   The darkness which hides my mountain range and peak
   And the light which billows and whispers in the mind,
   Are strings which vibrate and secretly compel me
   To guard you, Faroe Islands, my country!

3. My knee I will bend in prayer to you, God,
   Your peace, Oh Thou highest, as a message to me bring!
   My soul will bow at your baptismal blessing
   Then it may venture, I hope, with frankness and joy
   To carry forward the mark which witnesses the task
   That serves you, Faroe Islands, my land!

FINLAND

Maamme
OUR LAND

Words by
JOHAN LUDVIG RUNEBERG (1804-1877)

Translated by
CHARLES WHARTON STORK

Music by
FREDRIK PACIUS (1809-1891)

1. Oi Maam - me, Suo - mi, syn - nyin - maa! Soi sa - na kul - tai - nen! Ei laak - so - a,___ ei___ kuk - ku - laa, Ei

1. Our land, our land, our na - tive land, Oh, let her name ring clear! No peaks a - gainst___ the___ heav'ns that stand, No

This Anthem was written by Finland's National Poet
Sung for the first time at a students' gathering, 13th May 1848.

cresc.

vet - tä, ran - taa___ rak-kaam-paa, Kuin ko - ti-maa tää poh-joi -
gen - tle dales or___ foam-ing strand are lov'd as we our home re-

ff

- nen, Maa kal - lis i - si - en!
-vere, The earth our sires held dear.

2. *Sun kukoistukses kuorestaan*
   Kerrankin puhkeaa!
   Viel' lempemme saa nousemaan
   Sun toivos, riemus loistossaan,
   Ja kerran laulus, synnyinmaa,
   Korkeemman kaiun saa!

2. The flowers in their buds that grope
   Shall burst their sheaths with spring;
   So from our love to bloom shall ope
   Thy gleam, thy glow, thy joy, thy hope,
   And higher yet some day shall ring
   The patriot song we sing!

FRANCE
La Marseillaise

English translation of first verse by
PERCY BYSSHE SHELLEY (1792-1822)
of second verse by
MARY ELIZABETH SHAW

Words and Music by
CLAUDE-JOSEPH ROUGET de L'ISLE
(1760 - 1836)

Alla marcia

1. *Ai-lons en-fants de la Pa - tri - e, Le jour de*
1. Ye sons of France, a - wake to glo - ry, Hark, hark, what

gloire est ar - ri - vé. *Con - tre nous, de la ty - ran-*
my - riads bid you rise: Your child-ren, wives and grand - sires

- ni - e, *L'é - ten-dard sang - lant est le - vé,* *l'é - ten-*
hoa - ry, ★See their tears and hear their cries, see their

★Shelley has "behold"
Written and composed on 24th April, 1792
Adopted as National Anthem, 15th July, 1795

K

dard__ sang-lant est le - vé.   En-ten-dez-vous, dans les cam-
tears__ and hear their__ cries!   Shall hateful ty - rants mis - chief__

-pag - nes   Mu -   gir ces fa-rou - ches sol - dats.   Ils
breed - ing   With   hire - ling__ hosts, a ruf - fian band   Af-

vien - nent jus-que dans nos bras   é - gor - ger   vos fils, vos com-
-fright   and de-so-late the land,   While   peace   and li - ber-ty lie

-pag - nes.   Aux ar - mes ci - toy - ens!   For-
bleed-ing?   To   arms,___ to arms, ye brave!   Th'a-

2. *Amour sacré de la Patrie,*
   Conduis, soutiens nos bras vengeurs.
   Liberté, liberté chérie,
   Combats avec tes défenseurs; (bis)
   Sous nos drapeaux, que la victoire
   Accoure à tes mâles accents;
   Que tes ennemis expirants
   Voient ton triomphe et notre gloire!

   Aux armes citoyens, etc.

2. O sacred love of France, undying,
   Th'avenging arm uphold and guide.
   Thy defenders, death defying,
   Fight with Freedom at their side.
   Soon thy sons shall be victorious
   When the banner high is raised;
   And thy dying enemies, amazed,
   Shall behold thy triumph, great and glorious.

   To arms, to arms, ye brave! etc.

GABON
La Concorde

Words and Music by
GEORGES DAMAS
Arr. by HENRY COLEMAN

Tempo di Marcia

U - ni _____ dans la Con-cor - de et la _____

_____ fra - ter - ni - té, _____ E - veil - le-toi Ga - bon, une

au - ro-re se lè - ve, En - cou - ra - ge l'ar - deur qui

This became the National Anthem when Gabon achieved independence on 17th August 1960

vibre et nous sou-lè - ve!___ C'est en-fin notre es-sor vers la fé-

rall *2nd time*   *Fine*

-li - ci - té. C'est en-fin notre es-sor vers la fé-li - ci - té.

Fine

CHORUS

p dolce

E - blou - is - sant et fier,___ le jour

p

su - bli - me monte___ Pour-chas - sant à ja-mais___

l'in - jus - tice et la hon - te. Qu'il mon -

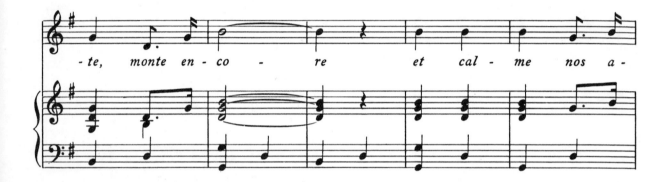

-te, monte en - co - re et cal - me nos a -

-lar - mes, Qu'il pro - ne la ver - tu ____

et re - pous - se les armes. ____

2   *Oui que le temps heureux rêvé par nos ancêtres*
    Arrive enfin chez nous, rejouisse les êtres,
    Et chasse les sorciers, ces perfides trompeurs
    Qui semaient le poison et répandaient la peur.

3   *Afin qu'aux yeux du monde et des nations amies*
    Le Gabon immortel reste digne d'envie,
    Oublions nos querelles, ensemble bâtissons
    L'édifice nouveau auquel tous nous rêvons.

4   *Des bords de l'Ocean au cœur de la forêt,*
    Demeurons vigilants, sans faiblesse et sans haine!
    Autour de ce drapeau, qui vers l'honneur nous mène,
    Saluons la Patrie et chantons sans arrêt:

Translation by
T.M. CARTLEDGE

Chorus   United in concord and brotherhood,
    Awake, Gabon, dawn is at hand.
    Stir up the spirit that thrills and inspires us!
    At last we rise up to attain happiness.

1   Dazzling and proud, the sublime day dawns,
    Dispelling for ever injustice and shame.
    May it still advance and calm our fears,
    May it promote virtue and banish warfare.

2   Yes, may the happy days of which our ancestors dreamed
    Come for us at last, rejoicing our hearts,
    And banish the sorcerers, those perfidious deceivers
    Who sowed poison and spread fear.

3   So that, in the eyes of the world and of friendly nations,
    The immortal Gabon may maintain her good repute,
    Let us forget our quarrels, let us build together
    The new structure of which we all have dreamed.

4   From the shores of the Ocean to the heart of the forest,
    Let us remain vigilant, without weakness and without hatred!
    Around this flag which leads us to honour,
    Let us salute the Fatherland and ever sing:

THE GAMBIA

Adapted by J. F. HOWE (1965)
from the traditional Mandinka song
"Foday Kaba Dumbuya"

Broadly (♩ = 80)

For the Gam - bi - a, our___ home - land, We___ strive and work and pray, That all may___ live in u - ni - ty, Free - dom and peace each day. Let jus - tice guide our ac - tions To -

Officially adopted 18 February 1965, when Gambia became independent.

GERMANY
Deutschland-Lied

Words by
HEINRICH HOFFMAN VON FALLERSLEBEN (1798-1874)

Music by
JOSEPH HAYDN (1732-1809)

Einigkeit und Recht und Freiheit für das deutsche Vaterland! Danach lasst uns alle streben brüderlich mit Herz und Hand! Einig-

Authorized as Germany's National Anthem on 11 August, 1922, when the first verse of Heinrich von Fallersleben's poem was sung. In 1950 the Federal Republic adopted the third verse instead as the official words.

-keit und Recht und Frei-heit sind des Glück - es Un - ter -

-pfand Blüh im Glan - ze die - ses

Glück - es blü - he___ deut - sches Va - ter - land!

Free Translation

Unity and right and freedom
for the German fatherland;
let us all pursue this purpose
brotherly, with heart and hands.
Unity and right and freedom
are the pawns of happiness.
Bis { Flourish in this blessing's glory
{ flourish, German fatherland

GHANA

Words by
various authors.
Verse 4 is by the composer

Music by
PHILIP GBEHO

Ritmico, con moto

1. Lift high the flag of Gha - na The gay star shin - ing in the sky, Bright with the souls of our fa - thers, Be - neath whose shade we'll live and die, we'll live and die. Red for the blood of the he - roes in the fight, Green for the

2. We'll live and die for Gha - na, Our land of hope for a - ges to come! Shout it a - loud, O Gha - na, And beat it out up - on the drum, up - on the drum! Come from the palm - lined shore, From the broad north - ern plain, From the

die.

drum!

Officially became the National Anthem in 1957, the year when independence was attained

fruit - ful ____ farms of ____ our birth - right, ____ And
farm and the for - est, The moun - tain and mine, ____ Your

linked with these the shin - ing gold - en band That marks the
child - ren sing with an - cient min - strel lore: Free - dom for

rich - ness of our Fa - ther - land, ____ And - land. ____
ev - er, ____ for ev - er, more. ____ Your more. ____

D.C.

3. This be our vow, O Ghana,
   To live as one, in unity,
   And in your strength, O Ghana,
   To build a new fraternity!
   Africa waits, in the night of the clouded years,
   For the spreading light that now appears
   To give us all a place beneath the sun,
   The destined ending of a task well done.

4. Lord God, our Father, we pray Thee,
   Be Thou our guide in all our ways.
   May we united together
   Proclaim the dawn of our new day.
   Children of Ghana, arise and uphold your cause,
   And spread the news of Freedom far and wide;
   O God our Father hearken to our call,
   And grant us peace here in our Fatherland.

GREAT BRITAIN

God Save The Queen

Origin of both words and melody obscure.
Earliest copy of words in Gentleman's Magazine, 1745.

God save our gra - cious Queen, Long live our no - ble Queen,

God save the Queen: Send her vic - to - ri - ous, Hap - py and

glo - ri - ous, Long to_ reign o - ver us: God save the Queen.

2. O Lord our God arise,
   Scatter her enemies,
   And make them fall:
   Confound their politics,
   Frustrate their knavish tricks,
   On Thee our hopes we fix:
   God save us all.

3. Thy choicest gifts in store,
   On her be pleased to pour;
   Long may she reign:
   May she defend our laws,
   And ever give us cause
   To sing with heart and voice
   God save the Queen.

GREECE

Words by
DIONYSIOS SOLOMÓS (1798-1857)
English versification by
T. M. CARTLEDGE

Music by
NIKOLAOS MANTZAROS (1795-1873)

Chosen as National Anthem of Greece by King George I and adopted in 1864.
Of the 158 verses, the first two which are given are those usually sung.
Music copyright J.B. Cramer & Co. Ltd.

kok - ka-la vyal-me - nee ton el - lee - non ta ye
Greeks of old whose dy - ing Brought to birth our spi - rit

ra _____ Ke san prawt' an - three - o-
free. _____ Now, with an - cient val - our

-me - nee hye - r'o hye - ri e - lef - the - rya. _____ Ke san
ris - ing, Let us hail you, oh Li - ber - ty! _____ Now, with

prawt' an - three - o - me - nee hye - r'o hye _____ *r'e-lef-the-*
an - cient val-our ris - ing, Let us hail you, Li - ber-

-rya, _____ *Ke san prawt'* ___ *an - three - o -*
-ty, _____ Now, with an - cient val - our

-me - nee hye - r'o hye - r'e-lef - the-rya. _____
ris - ing, Let us hail you, Li - ber - ty! _____

L

GREENLAND

nangminek erinalik

Words by
HENRIK LUND (1875-1948)

Music by
JONATHAN PETERSEN (1881-1961)
Arr. by HENRY COLEMAN

1. nu - nar - put, u-tor - kar - ssu - á - ngo - ra-vit ni

ar kut - u - lig - si - ma - vok kî - nik! kî - tor - na - tit kiv - ssu - mi-

- ái - nar - pa - tit, tu - niv - dlu-git si - ne - ri - a - vit pî - nik!

2. akugdlekutaussutut merdlertutut
ilingne perortugut tamâne
kalâtdlinik ingminik taiumavugut
niarkuvit atarkinartup sâne!

3. atortitdlugitdlo tamaisa pisit
ingerdlaniarusulekaugut
nutarterdlugitdlo nokitsigissatit
sujumut, sujumut piumakaugut

This is Greenland's National Song. The Danish National Anthem is also used.

4. *inersimalersut ingerdlanerat*
    tungâlítiterusuleкârput
    oкautsit »avîsit« канок kingunerat
    atúsassoк erinigileкârput.

5. *taкigdlune nâme atúngiveкaoк,*
    kâlátdlit, sujumut makigitse!
    inugtut inûneк pigiuminaкaoк
    saperase isumaкaleritse!

Free Translation

1. Our immemorial land under the beacon of gleaming ice
    With glowing snow hair around your head !
    You faithful mother, who carried us in your embrace,
    While ocean game of your coasts you promised us.

2. As immature children we have sprung from your soil
    And grown up with you among your mountains .
    Our name is Kalatdlit, in the deep track of legend
    Venerated for the age of its white countenance.

3. And all the while your wealth was used for our good,
    We longed for the new forms of the world :
    Released from the tight bands in the homeland circle
    Now advance ; forward towards distant objects we rush.

4. You grown-up nations, stretch out your hand !
    Your track we long soon to follow .
    A world of books shall urge forward the spirit
    Which carries us up on the wave of new learning.

5. Impossible now to tarry inactive longer
    Kalatdlit, stand up! Meet the new day !
    As free-born beings from now on we will grow,
    Begin to have faith in the dawn of ability!

GUATEMALA

Words by
JOSÉ JOAQUÍN PALMA (1844-1911)
Translated by
JOSÉ P. UGARTE
Versified by
MARTIN, MARY ELIZABETH and DICCON SHAW

Music by
RAFAEL ÁLVAREZ (b.1858)

Adopted by governmental decrees of 28 October, 1896 and 19 February, 1897, and modified by decree of 26 July, 1934

By permission of J.B. Cramer & Co. Ltd.

VERSE

¡Gua - te - ma - la fe - liz! que tus a - ras no pro-
Gua - te - ma - la, blest land, home of hap - py race, May thine

-fa - ne ja - más el ver - du - go; ni ha-ya es - cla - vos que la - man el
al - tars pro - fa - ned be nev - er; No yoke of sla - ver - y weigh on thee

yu - go ni ti - ra - nos que es-cu - pan tu faz. Si ma-
e - ver, Nor may ty - rants e'er spit in thy face. Should to-

-ña - na tu sue - lo sa - gra - - - do lo a - me - na - za in - va - sión ex - tran-
-mor - row see me - naced thy sa - cred soil By in - va - ders all pi - ty de-

-je - ra, li - - bre al vien - to tu her - mo - sa ban-
-ny - ing, Your loved flag to the winds free - ly

-de - ra a ven - cer o a mo - rir lla - ma - rá.
fly - ing Will call you to con - quer or die.

CHORUS

Li - bre al vien - to tu her - mo - sa ban - de - ra a ven-
Your loved flag to the winds free - ly fly - ing Will

-cer o a mo - rir lla - ma - rá; que tu pue - blo con á - ni - ma
call you to con - quer or die. You would soon - er be slain fight-ing

fie - ra an - tes muer - to q'es - cla - vo se - rá.
brave - ly Than sub - ject - ed in sla - ve - ry lie.

GUINEA

Liberté

Music by
ALFA YAYA
Arr. by KEITA FODÉBA
and J. CELLIER

No words

GUYANA

Words by
A. L. LUKER

Music by
R. C. G. POTTER

1. Dear land of Guy-a-na, of ri-vers and plains, Made rich by the sun-shine and lush by the rains, Set gem-like and
2. Green land of Guy-a-na, our he-roes of yore, Both bonds-men and free, laid their bones on your shore; This soil so they

The words and music were selected as the result of a competition. This anthem was approved by the House of Assembly on 21st April, 1966. Guyana became independent 26th May, 1966.

fair_____ be-tween moun - tains and sea,_____ Your
hal - lowed, and from them_____ are we,_____ All

child - ren sa - lute you, dear land_____ of the free.
sons of one mo - ther, Guy - a - na the free.

3. Great land of Guyana, diverse though our strains,
   We are born of their sacrifice, heirs of their pains,
   And ours is the glory their eyes did not see –
   One land of six peoples, united and free.

4. Dear land of Guyana, to you will we give
   Our homage, our service, each day that we live;
   God guard you, great Mother, and make us to be
   More worthy our heritage – land of the free.

HAITI
La Dessalinienne

Words by
JUSTIN LHÉRISSON
English versification by
MARTIN SHAW
(First verse by
DICCON SHAW and MARY ELIZABETH SHAW)

Music by
NICOLAS GEFFRARD

This anthem was composed for the centenary of national independence in 1903. The title is derived from Jean-Jacques Dessalines, the founder of Haiti as an independent republic, of which he crowned himself Emperor.

English words copyright J.B.Cramer & Co.Ltd.

-chons   u - nis,   mar - chons   u - nis Pour le Pa-
- ni - ted march, march   on!   U - ni - ted march for

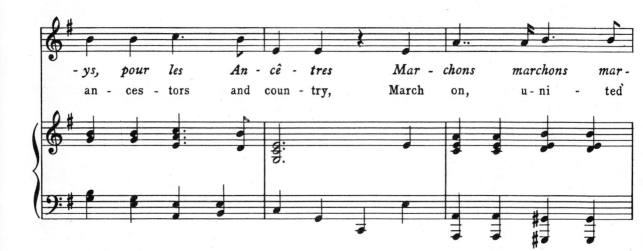

- ys, pour les An - cê - tres   Mar - chons marchons mar-
an - ces - tors   and coun - try,   March on, u - ni - ted

-chons   u - nis Pour le Pa - ys, pour les An - cê - tres!
march, march on! U-nite for an - ces - tors and coun - try!

2. *Pour les Aieux*
   Pour la Patrie
   Bêchons joyeux:
   Quand le champ fructifie
   L'âme se fortifie
   Bêchons joyeux
   Pour les Aïeux,
   Pour la Patrie.

3. *Pour le Pays*
   Et pour nos Pères
   Formons des Fils.
   Libres, forts et prospères,
   Toujours: nous serons frères,
   Formons des fils
   Pour le Pays
   Et pour nos Pères.

4. *Pour les Aïeux*
   Pour la Patrie
   O Dieu des Preux!
   Sous ta garde infinie
   Prends nos droits, notre vie,
   O Dieu des Preux!
   Pour les Aïeux,
   Pour la Patrie.

5. *Pour le Drapeau*
   Pour la Patrie,
   Mourir est beau!
   Notre passé nous crie:
   Ayez l'âme aguerrie!
   Mourir est beau
   Pour le Drapeau,
   Pour la Patrie.

2. For sacred soil,
   For sires of old
   We gladly toil.
   When teem field and wold
   The soul is strong and bold.
   We gladly toil, we gladly toil
   For sacred soil,
   For sires of old.

3. For land we love
   And sires of old
   We give our sons.
   Free, happy, and bold,
   One brotherhood we'll hold.
   We give our sons, we give our sons
   For land we love
   And sires of old.

4. For those who gave
   For country all,
   God of the brave,
   To thee, O God, we call;
   Without thee we must fall,
   God of the brave, God of the brave.
   For those who gave
   For country all.

5. For flag on high
   For Native land
   'Tis fine to die.
   Our traditions demand
   Be ready, heart and hand,
   'Tis fine to die, 'tis fine to die
   For flag on high,
   For Native land.

HONDURAS

Words by
AUGUSTO C. COELLO (1881-1941)
English versification by
J. E. HALES
(From the translation by
Señor TIBURCIO CARIAS h,)

Music by
CARLOS HARTLING
(1875-1919)

This anthem was selected as result of a public competition. It was adopted as the National Anthem in 1915.

By permission of J. B. Cramer & Co. Ltd.

ven en su fon - do sa - gra - do   cin - co es -
sa - cred ab - yss - es there twin - kle   Five pale

- tre - llas de pá - li - do a - zul;   en tu em -
stars lit with soft - est rays of blue.   And in your

- ble - ma que un mar ru - mo - ro - so   con sus
shield, that a stri - dent sea is guard - ing   With the

on - das bra - ví - as es - cu - da,   De un vol -
bul - wark of its sav - age bil - lows' might,___   A vol -

-cán,_____ de un vol - cán_____ tras la
ca - - no stands, a vol - ca - - no stands, from whose

ci - ma des - nu - da hay un as - - tro, hay un
lone - ly sum-mit's height_ Comes the bea - con clear, comes the

as - - tro de_ ni - ti - da luz.
bea - con clear, of a star that flash - es there.

Fine

Fine

Meno mosso
p VERSE

In - dia, vir - gen y her - mo - sa dor - mi - as de tus
In - dia, like a fair maid you were sleep - ing To the

p

Ped. Ped. sim.

ma - res al can - to so - no - ro, cuan-do e -
sound of the o - cean un - rest - ing; With - in the

-cha - da en tus cuen - cas de o - ro el au -
cra - dle of your gold - en val - leys nest - ing, When the bold

-daz na - ve - gan - te te ha - lló; y al mi -
nav - i - ga - tor sight - - ed you, And to the

-rar tu be - lle - za ex-ta-si-a - do al in -
spell of your po - tent charms a__ vic - tim, By all the

M

-flu - jo i-de-al de tu en - can - to, la
mar - vels of your love-li-ness en - chant - ed, De -

or la a - zul de tu es-plén - di - do
-vout - ly a kiss love-la - den he im-

man - to con su be - so de a-mor con-sa-gró.
-plant - ed On your man - tle's rich mar - gin of blue.

Last Verse

Por guardar ese emblema divino,	In defence of our glorious emblem
marcharemos Oh Patria a la muerte,	We are ready, my Country, to perish,
generosa será nuestra suerte,	For future ages their fame will ever cherish
si morimos pensando en tu amor.—	Who in their dying hour are thinking of your love.
Defendiendo tu santa bandera	In the defence of your holy banner fallen,
y en tus pliegues gloriosos cubiertos,	Their lifeless forms in its hallowed folds enshrouded.
serán muchos, Oh Honduras tus muertos,	Not few, blessed Honduras, shall be your proud dead,
pero todos caerán con honor.—	But they all in honour's cause will die.

HUNGARY

Words by
FERENC KÖLCSEY (1790-1838)

Music by
FERENC ERKEL (1810-1893)
Arr. by HENRY COLEMAN

Is - ten áldd meg a ma - gyart Jó kedv - vel bő -
God bless the Hun - gar - i - ans Give them joy and

- ség - gel. Nyújts fe - lè - je vé - dő kart,
plen - ty Pro - tect their bat - tal - i - ons

Ferenc Erkel was the creator of the Hungarian romantic Grand Opera. From 1875-1886 he was Director
of the National Academy of Music, and he founded in 1867 the National Association of Hungarian Choirs.
This was awarded first prize in a national competition in 1844 when it was officially adopted.

ICELAND
Lofsöngur

Words by
MATTHIAS JOCHUMSSON (1835-1920)

Music by
SVEINBJÖRN SVEINBJÖRNSSON
(1847-1926)

Written and composed in 1874, when Iceland secured its own constitution
and also celebrated the one thousandth anniversary of the first
permanent settlers of Europeans (Norwegians) on the island.

þús - und ár dag - ur, ei meir, eitt ei - lífð - ar smá blóm með

titr - and - i tár, sem til - bið - ur guð sinn og deyr. Ís - lands

þús - und ár, Ís - lands þús - und ár eitt ei - lífð - ar smá - blóm með

titr - and - i tár, sem til - bið - ur guð sinn og deyr.

Free Translation

Our country's God! Our country's God!
We worship Thy name in its wonder sublime
The suns of the heavens are set in Thy crown
By Thy legions, the ages of time!
With Thee is each day as a thousand years,
Each thousand of years, but a day.
Eternity's flow'r with its homage of tears,
That reverently passes away.
  Iceland's thousand years!
Eternity's flow'r, with its homage of tears,
That reverently passes away.

INDIA

Jană Gană Mană

Words and melody by
RABINDRANATH TAGORE (1861-1941)
Arr. by BRYSON GERRARD

Officially adopted by the Indian Constitutional Assembly on
24th January 1950, two days before the proclamation of the Republic.

Ya - mu-nă, Gan - gā, Uch' ha - lă ja - la-dhĩ ta ran - gă.

Ta - va shu-bhă nā - mé jā - gé, Ta-va shu-bhă ā - shī-shă

mā - gé, gā-ve ta-vă ja - yă gā - thā. Ja-nă ga-nă man - ga-lă

dā ya-kă ja-yă hé Bhā - ra-tă bhā - gyă vi - dhā - tā. Ja-yă

*See Footnote 2

pu - ra-bă pas-hchi-mă ā - té   té ré sim - ha sa - nă

pā - să   pré - mă-hā — ră ko gu - thé.

Ja-nă ga-nă ai kyă vi - dhā - ya-kă ja-yă hé! Bhā - ra-tă bhā - gyă vi-

dhā - tā.   Ja-yă hé!   Ja-yă hé!   Ja-yă hé!

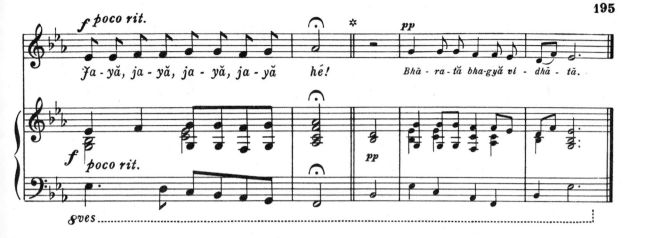

Ja - yă, ja - yă, ja - yă, ja - yă   hé!   Bhā - ra - tă bha-gyă vi - dhā - tă.

Free Translation

Thou art the ruler of the minds
    of all people,
Thou Dispenser of India's destiny,
Thy name rouses the hearts
    of the Punjab, Sind,
    Gujrat and Maratha, of Dravid,
    Orissa and Bengal.
It echoes in the hills of
    the Vindhyas and Himalayas,
    Mingles in the music of
    Jumna and Ganges,
    and is chanted by the waves
    of the Indian sea.
They pray for thy blessing
    and sing thy praise,
Thou Dispenser of India's destiny,
Victory, Victory, Victory to thee!

*Note 1. It will be noticed that the tune ends on the subdominant. The two bars in small notes at the end are not infrequently added — but they are not part of the original melody.

    2. For ordinary performances it is usual to end at the first asterisk.

    3. The Bengali words of the song have been transliterated for English readers and should therefore be pronounced as in English, i.e. 'J' as in the English 'John'. 'Hs' should be lightly aspirated, even in 'th' which is pronounced as in 'at home' said rather quickly. 'Sh' and 'ch', however, remain as in English; 'g' is always hard; 'é' as in French.

INDONESIA

Indonesia Raya

Words and Music by
WAGE RUDOLF SUPRATMAN
(1903-1938)

1. In - do - ne - sia___ ta - nah a -
2. In - do - ne - sia!___ Ta - nah jang
3. In - do - ne - sia!___ Ta - nah jang

- ir - ku Ta - nah tum - pah da - rah - ku. Di - sa -
mu - lia, Ta - nah ki - ta jang ka - ja. Di - sa -
su - tji, Ta - nah ki - ta jang sak - ti. Di - sa -

This was adopted as the Nationalist Party Song in 1928, and became the National Anthem in 1949.

198

-lah ta - nah-ku, Hi - dup - lah ne - gri - ku, Bang - sa-
-lah Ta - nah-nja, Su - bur - lah dji - wa - nja, Bang - sa-
-lah Rak - jat-nja, S'la - mat - lah pu - tra - nja, Pu lau-

-ku, Rak - jat-ku se - 'm - wa - nja. Ba - ngun-
-nja, Rak - jat-nja se - 'm - wa - nja. Sa - dar-
-nja, la - ut-nja se - 'm - wa - nja. Ma - dju-

-lah dji - wa - nja, Ba - ngun - lah ba - dan - nja Un - tuk
-lah ha - ti - nja, Sa - dar - lah bu - di - nja Un - tuk
-lah Ne - gri - nja, Ma - dju - lah Pan - du - nja Un - tuk

In - do - ne - sia Ra - ja.
In - do - ne - sia Ra - ja.
In - do - ne - sia Ra - ja.

ff
In - do-

-ne - sia Ra - ja, Mer - de - ka, Mer - de - ka, Ta - nah-

-ku ne - gri - ku jang ku - tjin - ta. In - do-

-ne - sia Ra - ja, Mer - de - ka, Mer - de - ka, Hi - dup-

molto ritard. 2nd time

-lah In - do - ne - sia Ra - ja. In - do- -ja.

molto ritard. 2nd time

Free Translation

1 INDONESIA, our native country
Consecrated with our spilt blood
Where we all arise to stand guard
Over this our Motherland:
Indonesia our nationality
Our people and our country.
Come then, let us all demand
Indonesia united.
Long live our land
Long live our state
Our nation, our people, and all
Arouse then its spirit,
Organise its own bodies
To obtain Indonesia the Great.

2 INDONESIA, an eminent country,
Our wealthy country
There we shall be forever.
Indonesia, the country of our
ancestors,
A relic of all of us.
Let us pray
For Indonesia's prosperity:
May her soil be fertile
And spirited her soul,
The nation and all the people.
Conscious be her heart
And her mind
For Indonesia the Great.

3 INDONESIA, a sacred country,
Our victorious country:
There we stand
Guarding our true Mother.
Indonesia, a beaming Country,
A country we love with all our heart,
Let's make a vow
That Indonesia be there forever.
Blessed be her people
And her sons,
All her islands, and her seas.
Fast be the country's progress
And the progress of her youth
For Indonesia the Great.

CHORUS   INDONESIA the Great, independent and free,
My beloved land and country.
Indonesia the Great, independent and free,
Long live Indonesia the Great.

IRAN
Imperial Salute

Words by
S. AFSAR
English versification by
FRANCIS GOULDING and T. M. CARTLEDGE
from a translation by MAS'UUD FARZAAD

Music by
Lieut. NAJMI MOGHADDAM

Allegro moderato

1. *Shah - han - sha - he - maw   zen - de baw daw*
1. Long   live   the Shah,   our   King   of Kings, And

Paw - yad kesh - var - be - far - rash   jaw - ve - dawn.   Kez
may   his   glo - ry make im - mor - tal   our land.   For

Pah - le - vee shood mulk - e I - rawn   Sad - rah beh - tar ze - e
Pah - le - vi   im - proved   I - ran   A   hun - dred - fold from where it

First used about 1934

N

2. *Ay! Par-chamm-i-khoor-sheed-i-I-rawn*
   Par-to af-kann be roo-yi-een Je-hawn
   Yawd aw-varr az oon roo-ze-gaw-ree
   Kaw-sood az bar-qi-tee-ghat harr ke-rawn.
   Dan saw-yè-yat jawn-mee-fa-shaw-neem
   Az dush-man-awn jawn mee-se-taw-neem
   Maw vaw-ress-i-mul-ki-kay-aw-neem
   Ham-ee-shè khaw-heem vat-tan-naw az del-lo-jawn.

3. *Boo-dee-mo has-teem pai-ru-vi-haqq.*
   Juz haqq harr-gez na-khaw-heem az Je-hawn
   Baw shah-pa-ras-tee mam-li-kat-raw
   Daw-reem az dass-ti-dush-man darr em-awn.
   Maw pai-ru-vi ker-dawr-i-neek-eem
   Ro-shan-dell az pan-daw-ri-neek-eem
   Rakh-shan-dè az goof-taw-ri-neek-eem
   Shoo-dzeen faz-zaw-'el bu-lan-daw vaw-zè I-rawn.

2. Oh, Sun that shines on Iran's banner,
   Shed upon each nation rays strong and fair.
   Those days keep in our recollection
   When thy flashing sword brought peace everywhere.
   We give our lives in thy shade benign,
   And take the lives of each enemy.
   We are the heirs of Kianis' line;
   Oh, belovèd land, ever wholly thine are we.

3. Of Right we've been and still are champions.
   What is right is all we ever demand.
   Through worship of the King, we ever
   From the enemy will guard this our land.
   "Good Deeds" the first virtue of our call,
   "Good Thoughts" the light our hearts and minds to guide,
   And through "Good Speech" shining, one and all,
   This is Iran's fame that will echo far and wide.

IRAQ

No words

Music by
L. ZAMBAKA

This became the National Anthem in 1959, when it was composed.

ISLE OF MAN
Arrane Ashoonagh Dy Vannin

Words by
WILLIAM HENRY GILL
(1839-1922)

Manx translation by
JOHN J. KNEEN
(1873-1939)

Music adapted by
WILLIAM HENRY GILL
(1839-1922)

from a Traditional Manx Air

Moderato

1. O__ Hal - loe nyn ghooie, O__ Ch'lie-geen ny s'bwaaie
2. Nyn__ El - lan fo - hee, Cha__ boir noid - yn ee.
1. O__ land of our birth. O__ gem of God's earth,
2. Our__ Is - land, thus blest, No__ foe can mo lest;

Ry ghed - din er ooir aa - lin Yee! Shickyr ta dty Ard - stoyl,
Nee bis-hagh nyn eeast-yn as grain; Nee'n Chiarn shin y 'reayll
O__ Is - land so strong and so fair; Built firm as Bar - rool,
Our grain and our fish shall in - crease; From bat - tle and sword

Farraght-yn myr Bar - rule, As__ freayll shin ayns seyrs-nys as shee.__
Voish strieughyn yn theill, As__ croo - in - agh lesh shee 'n Ashoon ain.__
Thy__ Throne of Home Rule Makes us free as thy sweet moun-tain air.__
Pro - tect-eth the Lord, And crown-eth__ our na - tion with peace.__

The main National Anthem is that for Great Britain. This anthem was dedicated to
The Lady Raglan, 1907. There are 8 verses in all.
W.H. Gill, a keen Manxman, was a collector and arranger of Manx music, of which he made a special
study. J.J. Kneen was an expert on the Manx language and author of several books on it. For his scho-
larship he was awarded the Order of St Olaf by H.M. The King of Norway, in recognition also of the historical
connection between Norway and the Isle of Man.

ISRAEL

Hatikvah
THE HOPE

Words by
NAFTALI HERZ IMBER
(1856-1909)

Melody traditional

Hatikva **is now firmly established as the Anthem of the State of Israèl as well as the Jewish National Anthem**

shnot al - pa - yim, Le - hiyot am chof - shi be - ar - zei - nu,__
E - rez__ zi - on viye-ru-sha-la - yim. Le hiyot am chof - shi
be - ar - zei - nu,__ E - rez zi - on vive-ru-sha-la - yim.

Free Translation

While yet within the heart-inwardly
The soul of the Jew yearns,
And towards the vistas of the East-eastwards
An eye to Zion looks.
'Tis not yet lost, our hope,
The hope of two thousand years,
To be a free people in our land
In the land of Zion and Jerusalem.

ITALY
Inno di Mameli

Words by
GOFFREDO MAMELI
(1827-1849)

Music by
MICHELE NOVARO
(1822-1885)

Fra -

Adopted as National Anthem 2nd June, 1946, on the
establishment of the Italian Republic.

-tel - li d'I - ta - lia, l'I - ta - lia s'è

de - sta, del - l'el - mo di Sci - pio s'è

cin - ta la te - sta. Do - v'è la vit -

rall. a tempo
f

-to - ria? Le por - ga la chio - ma, chè schia - va di

rall. f a tempo

Ro - ma Id - di - o la cre - ò.

Fratel - li d'I - ta - lia, l'I-ta - lia s'è

de - sta, dell'el - mo di Sci - pio s'è cin - ta la te - sta. Dov'è la vit-

-to - ria? Le por - ga la chio - ma, che schia - va di Ro - ma Iddio la cre-

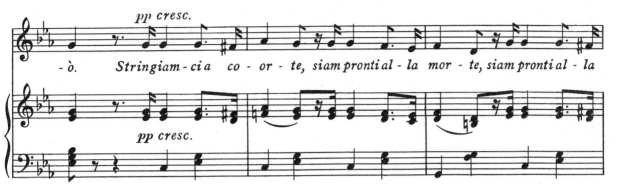

Free Translation

Italian Brothers,
Italy has arisen,
Has put on the helmet of Scipio.
Where is Victory?
Created by God
The slave of Rome,
She crowns you with glory.
Let us unite,
We are ready to die,
Italy calls.

IVORY COAST
l'Abidjanaise

Words by MATHIEU EKRA
in collaboration with JOACHIM BONY
and the Abbé COTY

Music by the Abbé
PIERRE MICHEL PANGO
Arr. by HENRY COLEMAN

Tempo di Marcia moderato

Sa - lut ô ter - re d'es - pé - ran - ce;
Tes fils___ chére Cote d'I - voi - re

Pa - ys de l'hos - pi - ta - li - té.___ Tes lé - gions rem-plies de vail -
Fiers ar - ti-sans de ta gran-deur,___ Tous ras-sem-blés et pour ta

-lan - ce Ont re-le - vé ta di - gni - té.___
gloi - re Te bâ-ti - ront dans le bon -

This National Anthem was adopted at the declaration of independence on 7th August, 1960
The music was composed by an Ivory Coast priest.
Mathieu Ekra is Minister of Information and Joachim Bony Minister of Education in the Ivory Coast.

-heur. _____ Fiers I - voi - riens, le pa - ys nous ap -

-pel - le. Si nous a - vons dans la paix ra - me -

-né la li - ber - té, No - tre de - voir se - ra d'être

un mo - dè - le De l'es - pé - ran - ce _____ pro - mise

à l'hu-ma-ni-té, En for-geant, u - nie dans la

foi nou-vel - le, la pa-trie de la vraie fra-ter-ni - té.

English Paraphrase by
ELIZABETH P. COLEMAN

We salute you, O land of hope, country of hospitality;
thy gallant legions have restored thy dignity.

Belovèd Ivory Coast, thy sons, proud builders of thy
greatness, all mustered together for thy glory,
in joy will construct thee.

Proud citizens of the Ivory Coast, the country calls us.
If we have brought back liberty peacefully, it will be
our duty to be an example of the hope promised to humanity,
forging unitedly in new faith the Fatherland of true
brotherhood.

JAMAICA

Words by
The Rev. HUGH SHERLOCK (b.1905)

Music by
ROBERT LIGHTBOURNE
Arr. by MAPLETOFT POULLE

1. E - ter - nal Fa - ther bless our land, Guard us with Thy
2. Teach us true re - spect for all, Stir re - sponse to

Migh - ty Hand, Keep us free from e - vil powers, Be our light through
du - ty's call, Streng-then us the weak to cher-ish, Give us vi - sion

count - less hours. To our Lead - ers, Great De - fen - der,
lest we per - ish. Know - ledge send us, Heaven - ly Fa - ther,

This was officially selected as the National Anthem by the House of Representatives in Jamaica on 19th July 1962. Robert Lightbourne is a Jamaican and Minister of Trade and Industry at the time of composing the Anthem. The Rev. Sherlock, a Jamaican, has for many years been associated with "Boys' Town" in one of the poorer districts of Kingston.

JAPAN

THE PEACEFUL REIGN

Words selected from the
seventh volume of *Kokinshu*
dating from the 9th century

English translation by
SAKUZO TAKADA

Music composed by
court musicians and
selected in 1880 by
HIROMORI HAYASHI

First performed on 3rd November, 1880, on the Emperor Meiji's birthday,
and approved as National Anthem on 12th August, 1893.

JOHORE
Lago Bangsa Johore

Malay words by
Captain H.M. Said BIN H. SULIEMAN S.M.J.
English words by
H.A. COURTNEY

Music by
M. GALISTAN

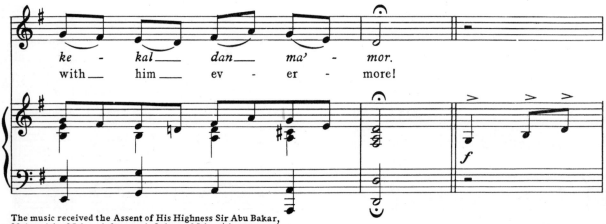

The music received the Assent of His Highness Sir Abu Bakar,
Maharajah of Johore (afterwards Sultan of Johore) in 1879.
The words received the Assent of His Highness Sir Ibrahim,
Sultan of Johore, in 1915.

Luas - kan kua - sa, Men - aong kan ka - mi, Ra -
Long may his hand,_____ Pro - tect our land, And

- yat di - pim - pi - ni, Ber - ze - man____ la - gi, Den -
lead his peo - ple on, Through years____ to____ be, In

gan mer - deh - ka ber - sa - tu ha - ti All - ah ber - ka - ti Jo - hore,
free - dom____ and in u - ni - ty____ God____ bless Jo - hore,

All - ah sla - mat kan Sul - - tan!
God____ save___ the Sul - - tan!

JORDAN

Words by
Professor 'ABDULMUN 'IM AR-RIFAA'I

Music by
Professor ABDULKADIR AT-TANNIR

Free Translation

Long live the King
Long live the King
His position is sublime
His banners waving in glory supreme.

Adopted as National Anthem when Emir Abdullah became King, 25 May, 1946.

KENYA

Traditional Kenya melody

The first line of each verse, * to *, may be sung by a soloist in the African traditional style.

The Kenya National Anthem is based on a traditional Kenya Folk Song which was adapted and harmonized by a National Commission of Musicians who also wrote the words. This honorary Commission comprised Graham Hyslop, M.A., Dip.Mus.; George W. Senoga-Zake, L.R.S.M.; Peter Kibukosya; Thomas Kalume; and Washington Omondi.

2. Let one and all arise
   With hearts both strong and true.
   Service be our earnest endeavour,
   And our Homeland of Kenya,
   Heritage of splendour,
   Firm may we stand to defend.

3. Let all with one accord
   In common bond united,
   Build this our nation together,
   And the glory of Kenya,
   The fruit of our labour
   Fill every heart with thanksgiving.

KOREA

English versification by
WHAMI KOH and
T. M. CARTLEDGE

Music by
EAKTAI AHN

This song, of unknown authorship, was set originally to a different tune and sung in Korea for many years.
When the Government of the Republic of Korea was established on 15th August, 1948, these verses, with the music
by Eaktai Ahn, were officially adopted as the National Anthem.

CHORUS

KUWAIT

No words

This is played on ceremonial occasions.

LAOS

Words by
MAHA PHOUMI
English versification by
T. M. CARTLEDGE

Music by
S. E. THONGDY

Xad - lao tang - tè - deum - ma khung - xu - lu -
Once our La - o - tian race in A - sia

-xa you - ney - a - xy Xao - lao pouk - phan - mey -
high - ly hon - oured stood, And at that time the

-try houam - sa - ma - khy hak - ho - hom kan. Hak -
folk of La - os were u - ni - ted in love. To -

The music is reproduced by permission of Institut für Auslands-
beziehungen, Stuttgart, from *Die National-Hymnen Der Erde*.
Adopted as National Anthem, 1947.   Written and first used 1941.

French Words

Notre race Lao a jadis connu en Asie une grande renommée.

Alors les Lao étaient unis et s'aimaient.

Aujourd'hui encore ils savent aimer leur race et leur pays et se groupent autour de leurs chefs.

Ils ont conservé la religion de leurs pères et ils savent garder le sol des aïeux.

Ils ne permettront pas que quelque nation vienne les troubler ou s'emparer de leur terre.

Quiconque voudrait envahir leur pays les trouverait résolus à combattre jusqu'à la mort.

Tous ensemble ils sauront restaurer l'antiquè gloire du sang lao et s'entr'aider aux jours d'épreuves.

LATVIA

Translated by
Dr. GEORGE A. SIMONS

Words and Music by
KARLIS BAUMANIS
(1834-1904)

Dievs, svē - ti Lat - vi - ju, mūs' dār - go tē - vi - ju, svē - ti jel Lat - vi - ju, ak svē - ti jel to! to! Kur lat - vju

Bless Lat - vi - a, O God, Our ver - dant na - tive sod. Where Bal - tic he - roes trod, Keep her from harm! harm! Our love - ly

Originally written as an entry for a singing festival in 1873, it very soon became the National Anthem
Since 1940 the National Anthem of the U.S.S.R. has been sung inside Latvia.

mei - tas zied,   kur   lat - vju   dē - li dzied,
daugh - ters near,   Our   sing - ing   sons   ap - pear,

cresc.

laid   mums tur   lai - mē diet,   mūs
May   For - tune   smil - ing here

f

1 Lat - vi - jā.
Grace Lat - vi - a.

2 Lat - vi - jā.
Grace Lat - vi - a!

LEBANON

Words by
RACHID NAKHLÉ

Music by
WADIA SABRA

Martial

1. Koul - lou - na   lil - oua - tann Lil -'ou - la   lil 'a
2. Chay - khou - na   oual - fa - ta   in - da - saôu - til   oua
3. Bah - rou - hou   bar - rou - hou Dour - ra - touch - char

Adopted officially by
Presidential decree on 12th July, 1927

lam,   Mil - ou 'ay   niz - za - man Say - fou - na oual ka -
tann   Ous - dou ghâ   bin ma - ta Sa - oua - rat nal - fi -
kain   Ril - dou - hou   bir - rou - hou Ma - li - oul kout -

- lam,   Sah - lou - na oual - ja - bal____ man - bi
- tann   Char - kou - na kal - bou - hou____ a - ba
- baïn   is - mou - hou 'iz - zou - hou____ moun zou

tonn lir - ri - jâl, Kaou - lou - na oual 'a - mal____ Fi - sa
dann loub - nane Sa - na - hou rab bou - hou____ Li - ma
kâ - nal jou - doude Maj - dou - hu ar - zou - hou____ Ram - zou -

-bî - lil ka mâl.
-dal az - mane. Koul - lou - na lil - oua - tann Lil' ou-
-hou lil - khou - loude

-la lil 'a - lam, koul - lou - na. lil - oua - tann.

Free Translation

1. All of us! For our Country, for our Flag and Glory!
   Our valour and our writings are the envy of the ages.
   Our mountains and our valleys, they bring forth stalwart men.
   And to Perfection all our efforts we devote.
   All of us! For our Country, for our Flag and Glory!

2. Our Elders and our children, they await our Country's call:
   And on the Day of Crisis they are as Lions of the Jungle.
   The heart of our East is ever Lebanon:
   May God preserve her until end of time.
   All of us! For our Country, for our Flag and Glory!

3. The Gems of the East are her land and sea.
   Throughout the world her good deeds flow from pole to pole.
   And her name is her glory since time began.
   Immortality's Symbol– the Cedar– is her Pride
   All of us! For our Country, for our Flag and Glory!

P

LESOTHO

Words by
FRANÇOIS COILLARD

Music by L. LAUR
(19th century)

2. *Molimo ak'u boloke Lesotho,*
   U felise lintoa le matŝoenyeho.
   Oho fatŝe lena,
   La bo-ntat'a rona,
   Le be le khotso.

1. Lesotho, land of our Fathers,
   You are the most beautiful country of all.
   You give us birth,
   In you we are reared
   And you are dear to us.

2. Lord, we ask You to protect Lesotho.
   Keep us free from conflict and tribulations.
   Oh, land of mine,
   Land of our Fathers,
   May you have peace.

The Government adopted this as their National Anthem on 2nd May. 1967,
using the first and last verses of the words written by a French missionary.

LIBERIA

Words by
DANIEL BASHER WARNER*

Music by
OLMSTEAD LUCA

1. All hail, Li - be - ria, hail! All hail, Li - be - ria, hail! This glo - rious land of li - ber - ty Shall long be ours___ Though new her name, Green be her fame, And

2. All hail, Li - be - ria, hail! All hail, Li - be - ria, hail! In u - nion strong suc - cess is sure— We can - not fail!___ With God a - bove Our rights to prove We

*Third President of Liberia, 1864 - 1868

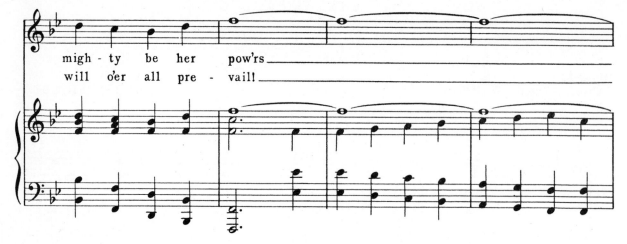

migh - ty be her pow'rs
will o'er all pre - vail!

And migh - ty be her pow'rs
We will o'er all pre - vail!

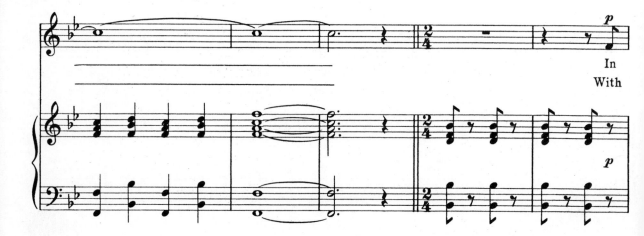

In
With

joy and glad - ness With our hearts u - ni - ted, We'll shout the
heart and hand Our coun-try's cause de-fend - ing We'll meet the

free - dom Of a race be-night - ed,⎫ Long live Li - be - ria,
foe With va - lour un - pre - tend - ing.⎭

hap - py land! A home of glo-rious li - ber-ty, By God's com -

-mand! A home of glo-rious li - ber-ty, By God's com - mand!

LIBYA

Words by
AL BASCHIR AL AREBI

Music by
MOHAMMED ABDUL WAHAB

Ya Bi-la - di Ya Bi-la - di Bi-ji-ha-di Wa-ji-la -

-di Id-fa-'i Kay-dal A-'a - di Wal-'a-wa - di Was-la -

-mi Is-la-mi Ii-la-mi Is-la-mi Tu-lal Ma-

This National Anthem was written and adopted in 1954,
three years after the attainment of independence.

- tan Lib - ya Lib - ya.

Free Translation

CHORUS

Oh my country! With my struggle and my patience
Drive off enemies and mishaps,
    And survive!
Survive all through
We are your ransom
    Oh Libya!

VERSE

Oh my country! You are the heritage of grandfathers,
May God cast off any hand that would harm you
Do survive! We are for ever your soldiers,
If you survive we care not who perishes.
To you we give solemn pledges
That we, Oh Libya, will never fail you.
    We will never
      Go back to fetters,
We have been liberated, and we have freed our home country
    Libya.

LIECHTENSTEIN

Words by
H. H. JAUCH (1850)

Composer unknown

1. O - ben am deut - schen Rhein leh - net sich Liech - ten - stein
2. Wo einst Sankt Lu - zi - en Frie - den nach Rä - ti - en

an Al - pen - höh'n. Dies lie - be Hei - mat - land im deut - schen
hin - ein ge - bracht, dort an dem Gren - zen - stein und längs dem

Va - ter - land hat Got - tes__ wei - se Hand für uns er - seh'n.
jun - gen Rhein steht furcht - los__ Liech - ten - stein auf Deutschlands Wacht.

The tune is the same as that of the National Anthem of Great Britain.

3. *Lieblich zur Sommerzeit*
   Auf hoher Alpenweid
   Schwebt Himmelsruh,
   Wo frei die Gemse springt,
   Kühn sich der Adler schwingt,
   Der Senn' das Ave singt
   Der Heimat zu.

4. *Von grüngen Felsenhöhn*
   Freundlich ist es zu sehn
   Mit einem Blick,
   Wie des Rheines Silberband
   Säumet das schöne Land,
   Ein kleines Vaterland
   Voll stillen Glücks.

5. *Hoch lebe Liechtenstein,*
   Blühend am deutschen Rhein,
   Glücklich und treu.
   Hoch leb der Fürst vom Land,
   Hoch unser Vaterland,
   Durch Bruderliebe Band
   Vereint und frei.

Free Translation

1. High above the German Rhine
   leans Liechtenstein
   against Alpine slopes.
   This beloved homeland
   in the German fatherland
   was chosen for us by
   the Lord's wisdom.

2. Where once St. Lucius
   brought peace to Rätien,
   there on the boundary-stone
   and along the young Rhine
   stands dauntless Liechtenstein
   on Germany's guard.

3. Lovely in summer-time
   on high Alpine pastures
   floats heavenly peace,
   where the chamois freely jumps about,
   the eagle sways boldy in the air,
   the herdsman sings the 'Ave'
   towards the homeland.

4. From high green rocks
   it is a lovely sight to watch
   how the silvery ribbon of the Rhine
   edges the beautiful country,
   a small fatherland,
   full of quiet happiness.

5. Long live Liechtenstein,
   blossoming on the German Rhine,
   happy and faithful.
   Long live the Duke of the Land,
   Long live our fatherland,
   united by brotherly bonds and free.

LITHUANIA

Words and Music by
VINCAS KUDIRKA (1858-1899)

This became the National Anthem 1918 and first appeared in print in 1896
In Lithuania the National Anthem of the U.S.S.R. is now used.

3. *Tegul saulė Lietuvos*
   Tamsumus prašalina,
   Ir šviesa, ir tiesa
   Mūs žingsnius telydi.

4. *Tegul meilė Lietuvos*
   Dega mūsų širdyse,
   Vardan tos Lietuvos
   Vienybė težydi!

1. Lithuania, land of heroes,
   Thou our Fatherland that art,
   From the glorious deeds of ages
   Shall Thy children take heart.

2. May Thy children ever follow
   Their heroic fathers
   In devotion to their country
   And good will to others.

3. May the sun of our loved shore
   Shine upon us evermore;
   May the right and the truth
   Keep our pathway lighted.

4. May the love of our dear land
   Make us strong of heart and hand,
   May our land ever stand
   Peaceful and united.

LUXEMBOURG

Ons Hémécht

OUR MOTHERLAND

Words by
MICHAEL LENTZ
(1820-1893)

Translated by
NICHOLAS E. WEYDERT

Music by
A. ZINNEN
(1827-1898)
Arr. by MARTIN SHAW
(1875-1958)

1. Wŏ d'Uol-zécht du-réch d'Wi-sen zĕt durch d'Fiel-zen d'Sau-er
1. Where slow you see the Al-zet-te flow, The Su-ra play wild

brécht, Wŏ d'Riéf lauscht d'Mu-sel dof-tég blet, den Him-mel Wein ons
pranks, Where love-ly vine-yards am-ply grow Up-on the Mo-selle's

mécht; Dât ass ons Land fir dât mer gĕf hei
banks, There lies the land for which our thanks Are

First performed 5th June, 1864, this became the National Anthem in 1895 replacing
De Feierwon (The Festal Train) by the same author (a well-known poet) and composer.
De Feierwon was written in 1859 to celebrate the opening of the first international
railway system connecting the Grand Duchy with the outside world. It is still a
popular hymn in Luxembourg.

-ni - den al - les w'on,   onst Hé - méchts-land dât
owed to God a - bove,   Our own, our na - tive

mir sŏ dĕf an on - sen Hier - zer dro'n._____ Onst
land which ranks Well fore - most in our love._____ Our

Hé - méchts-land dât mir sŏ dĕf an on - sen Hier-zer dro'n!_____
own, our na - tive land which ranks Well fore - most in our love._____

2. *O Du do uewen, dém seng Hand*
   Durch d'Welt d'Natio'ne lêd,
   Behitt Du d'Letzeburger Land
   Vum friéme Joch a Lêd.
   Du hues ons all als Kanner schon
   De freie Gèscht jo gin;
   LôB viru blénken d'Freihêtssonn,
   De' mir 'so' lâng gesin.
   LôB viru blénken d'Freihêtssonn,
   De' mir 'so' lâng gesin.

2. Oh Father in Heaven Whose powerful hand
   Makes states or lays them low,
   Protect the Luxembourger land
   From foreign yoke and woe.
   God's golden liberty bestow
   On us now as of yore.
   Let Freedom's sun in glory glow
   For now and evermore.

MADAGASCAR
O, Our Beloved Fatherland

Words by P. RAHAJASON

Music by
NORBERT RAHARISOA
Arr. by HENRY COLEMAN

This National Anthem was adopted on 21st October, 1958. Madagascar celebrated the birth of the Malagasy Republic on 26th June, 1960.

CHORUS

-hi - onao ry Za-na-ha - ry 'Ty No - si-ndrazanay i-

- ty_____ Hi - a - da-na sy ho fi - na - ri-tra He

sa-mba-tra to-koa i - za-hay_____ Ta hay.

1. O, our beloved fatherland,
   O, fair Madagascar,
   Our love will never decay
   But will last eternally.

2. O, our beloved fatherland,
   Let us be thy servant
   With body, heart and spirit
   In dear and worthy service.

3. O, our beloved fatherland,
   May God bless thee,
   That created all lands;
   In order He maintains thee.

CHORUS O, Lord Creator do Thou bless
        This Island of our Fathers
        That she may be happy and prosperous
        For our own satisfaction.

MALAWI
O God bless Malawi

Words* and Music by
MICHAEL-FRED P. SAUKA

1. O God bless our land of Ma-la-wi,
1. *Mlu - ngu da - li - tsa-ni Ma - la - wi,*
1. *Chi - u - ta mtu - mbi-ke Ma - la - wi,*

Keep it a land of peace. Put down each and
Mum - su - nge m'mte - nde - re. Go - nje - tsa - ni
Mu - mu-pe mu - te - nde. Mu - the - re - ske

ev - ery e - ne - my, Hung - er, dis - ease, en - vy.
a - da - ni o - nse, Nja - la, nthe - nda, nsa - nje.
ba - rwa - ni wo - se, Nja - ra, nthe - nda, sa - nje.

*The official text is given in English, Chinyanja and Chitumbuka.

Join to - ge - ther all our hearts as one,
Lu - nzi - tsa - ni mi - ti - ma ya - thu,
Gu - ma - nya - ni mi - ti - ma yi - thu,

That we be free from fear. Bless our lead - er,
Ku - ti ti - sa - o - pe. Mda - li - tse Mtso -
Nkhu - mbi ti - ba - vye - so. Mtu - mbi - ke Mlo -

each and ev - ery one, And Mo - ther Ma - la - wi.
-go le - ri na - fe, Ndi Ma - i Ma - la - wi.
-ngo - zgi na - to - se, Na ma - ma Ma - la - wi.

ENGLISH

2. Our own Malawi, this land so fair,
   Fertile and brave and free.
   With its lakes, refreshing mountain air,
   How greatly blest are we.
   Hills and valleys, soil so rich and rare,
   Give us a bounty free.
   Wood and forest, plains so broad and fair,
   All beauteous Malawi.

3. Freedom ever, let us all unite,
   To build up Malawi.
   With our love, our zeal and loyalty,
   Bringing our best to her.
   In time of war, or in time of peace,
   One purpose and one goal.
   Men and women serving selflessly,
   In building Malawi.

CHINYANJA

2. *Malawi ndziko lokongola,*
   La chonde ndi ufulu,
   Nyanja ndi mphepo ya m'mapiri,
   Ndithudi tadala.
   Zigwa, mapiri, nthaka, dzinthu,
   N'mphatso zaulere.
   Nkhalango, madambo abwino.
   Ngwokoma Malawi.

3. *O! Ufulu tigwirizane,*
   Kukweza Malawi.
   Ndi chikondi, khama, kumvera,
   Timutumikire.
   Pa nkhondo nkana pa mtendere,
   Cholinga n'chimodzi.
   Mai, bambo, tidziipereke,
   Pokweza Malawi.

CHITUMBUKA

2. *Malawi charo chakutowa,*
   Nyata na wanangwa,
   Nyanja, mphepo za mumapiri.
   Ta ba mwabi ndise,
   M'madambo nthaka ya vundira,
   Vyatipa wanangwa.
   Nguyi na madambo ghaweme,
   Kutowa Malawi.

3. *Wanangwa muyaya pamoza,*
   Tizenge Malawi.
   Kutemwa na mwamphu na nchindi
   Timutebetere.
   Mnyengo ya nkhondo nesi mtende,
   Chikhomo chimoza.
   Mama, dada, mwe tijipate,
   Mkukuzga Malawi.

MALAYSIA
NEGARA KU
MY COUNTRY

Words compiled by
a special Committee

Melody derived from
old Malay folk tune

Ne - ga - ra ku   Ta - nah tum-pah-nya da - rah ku____ Ra' yat hi - dup ber-sa - tu dan ma - ju____ Rah-mat bah - gia tu - han kur-ni - a

For short version cut from A to B

Adopted as National Anthem when Malaya achieved Independence
on 31st August, 1957. It was previously known in Malaya and Ind-
-onesia as a popular song called Terang Bulan (Moonlight): but this
popular version of the tune is now banned.   When Malaysia was
founded in 1963 this was retained as the National Anthem.

kan_____ Ra - ja ki - ta se - la - mat ber - takh -

ta_____ Rah-mat bah - gia tu - han kur-ni - a kan_____

_ Ra - ja ki - ta se - la - mat ber - takh - ta._____

Free Translation

My Country,
The land of my birth.
May her people live in unity and prosperity,
May God grant His blessings upon her,
Peacefully may our Ruler reign.
May God grant His blessings upon her,
Peacefully may our Ruler reign.

MALDIVE ISLANDS

Maestoso
melody well marked

This National Anthem is based on Auld Lang Syne.
It was first used in the Maldive Islands on the first
Rabiulawal, 1365 (Arabic calendar, i.e. February 1946)

Transliteration

Gavmii mi ekuverikan matii tibegen kuriime salaam,
Gavmii bahun gina heyo du'aa kuramun kuriime salaam.
Gavmii nishaanang hurmataa eku boo lambai tibegen
Audaanakan libigen e vaa dida-ak kuriime salaam.
Nasraa nasiibaa kaamyaabu-ge ramzakang himenee
Fessaa rataai hudaa ekii fenumun kuriime salaam.
Fakhraa sharaf gavmang e hoodai devvi batalunna'
Zikraage mativeri tentakun adugai kuriime salaam.
Divehiinge ummay kuri arai silmaa salaamatugai
Divehiinge nan motu vun adai tibegen kuriime salaam.
Minivankamaa madaniyyataa libigen mi 'aalamugai
Dinigen hitaama tibun edigen kuriime salaam.
Diinaai takhtang heyo hitun hurmay adaa kuramun
Siidaa vafaaterikan matii tibegen kuriime salaam.
Davlatuge aburaa 'izzataa mativeri vegen abada'
Audaana vun edi heyo du'aa kuramun kuriime salaam.

English Translation

We salute you in this national unity.
We salute you, with many good wishes in the national tongue,
Bowing the head in respect to the national symbol.
We salute the flag that has such might;
It falls into the sphere of victory, fortune and success
With its green and red and white together, and therefore we salute it.
To those heroes who sought out honour and pride for the nation
We give salute to-day in auspicious verses of remembrance.
May the nation of the Maldivian Islanders advance under guard and protection
And the name of the Maldivian Islanders become great. Thus we pledge as we salute.
We wish for their freedom and progress in this world
And for their freedom from sorrows, and thus we salute.
With full respect and heartfelt blessing towards religion and throne
We salute you in uprightness and truth.
May the State ever have auspicious honour and respect.
With good wishes for your continuing might, we salute you.

MALI

Music by
BANZOUMANA SISSOKO
Arr. by HENRY COLEMAN

A ton ap-pel, MA-LI, Pour ta pros-pé-ri-té Fi-

dèle à ton des-tin Nous se-rons tous u-nis, Un peuple, un

but, u-ne foi. ——— Pour une A-frique u-nie Si l'én-ne-

-mi découvre son front Au de-dans ou au de-hors De - bout sur les rem-

This National Anthem was adopted by the National Assembly of Mali on 9th August 1962

-parts Nous som-mes ré - so - lus de mou - rir.

Chorus

Pour l'A - frique et pour toi MA - LI
-LI au - jour-d'hui O MA-LI de de - main Les champs fleu-

rall. 2nd time

No - tre dra - peau se - ra li - ber - té.
-ris - sent d'es - pé - ran - ce, Les coeurs vi - brent de con -

Pour l'A-frique et pour toi MA - LI

No - tre com - bat se - ra u - ni - té.   O   MA- fian - ce.

2. *Debout, villes et campagnes,*
   Debout, femmes, jeunes et vieux
   Pour la Patrie en marche
   Vers l'avenir radieux
   Pour notre dignité.
   Renforçons bien nos rangs,
   Pour le salut public
   Forgeons le bien commun
   Ensemble, au coude à coude
   Faisons le chantier du bonheur.

3. *La voie est dure, très dure*
   Qui mène au bonheur commun.
   Courage et dévouement,   } (bis.)
   Vigilance à tout moment,
   Vérité des temps anciens,
   Vérité de tous les jours,
   Le bonheur par le labeur
   Fera le MALI de demain.

4. *L'Afrique se lève enfin*
   Saluons ce jour nouveau.
   Saluons la liberté,
   Marchons vers l'unité.
   Dignité retrouvée
   Soutient notre combat.
   Fidèles à notre serment
   De faire l'Afrique unie
   Ensemble, debout mes frères
   Tous au rendez-vous de l'honneur.

English Translation by
T.M. CARTLEDGE

1. At your call, MALI,
So that you may prosper,
Faithful to your destiny,
We shall all be united,
One people, one goal, one faith
For a united Africa.
If the enemy should show himself
Within or without,
On the ramparts
We are ready to stand and die.

Chorus   For Africa and for you, MALI,
Our banner shall be liberty.
For Africa and for you, MALI,
Our fight shall be for unity.
Oh, MALI of today,
Oh, MALI of tomorrow,
The fields are flowering with hope
And hearts are thrilling with confidence.

2. Stand up, towns and countryside,
Stand up, women, stand up young and old,
For the Fatherland on the road
Towards a radiant future.
For the sake of our dignity
Let us strengthen our ranks;
For the public well-being
Let us forge the common good.
Together, shoulder to shoulder,
Let us work for happiness.

3. The road is hard, very hard,
That leads to common happiness.
Courage and devotion,
Constant vigilance,
Courage and devotion,
Constant vigilance,
Truth from olden times,
The truths of every day,
Happiness through effort
Will build the MALI of tomorrow.

4. Africa is at last arising,
Let us greet this new day.
Let us greet freedom,
Let us march towards unity.
Refound dignity
Supports our struggle.
Faithful to our oath
To make a united Africa,
Together, arise, my brothers,
All to the place where honour calls.

MALTA

Innu Malti

HYMN OF MALTA

Words by
DUN KARM PSAILA (1871-1961)
Translated by
MAY BUTCHER

Music by
ROBERT SAMMUT M.D.
(1870-1934)

Maestoso   mf

1. Guard her, O Lord, _____ as _____
   Lil din l-Art he - lwa, _____ l-Omm li

2. May he who rules _____ for _____
   Agh - ti, Kbir Al - la, _____ id deh'n

ev - er Thou hast _____ guard - ed _____ This Mo - ther -
tat - na _____ i si - mha _____ Ha res, Mu -

wis - dom be _____ re - gard - ed, _____ In mas - ter
lil min _____ jah ki - mha, _____ Rodd il - hnie -

Dun Karm Psaila, Malta's greatest poet, was asked to write these words for a school hymn to
Sammut's music. He conceived the idea of writing a hymn to Malta in the form of a prayer; he
wanted to unite all parties with the strong ties of religion and love of country.
It was first performed on 3rd February, 1923, and later declared to be the official anthem (On
7th April, 1941).

land _____ so dear whose name ___ we ___ bear! _____
- lej, _____ Kif dej - jem Int ___ ha - rist: _____
mer - cy, strength in man ___ in - crease! _____
- na _____ lis - sid, sah - ha ___ 'l - had - di - em.

Keep her in mind ____ whom Thou hast made so ___ fair! _____
Fta - kar li lil - ha bil - oh - la dawl lib - bist! _____
Con - firm us all _____ in u - ni - ty and ___ peace! _____
Sed - daq il - ghaq - da fil - Mal - tin u ___ s - sliem!

MAURITANIA

Based on traditional music, this was adopted as the
National Anthem in 1960, the year of Independence.

come sopra

Ped.   Ped.

simile

eome sopra

Ped.   Ped.   Ped.   Ped.   simile

D. ℀ al Fine

R

MAURITIUS
Motherland

Words by
JEAN GEORGES PROSPER

Music by
PHILIPPE GENTIL

Glo - - - ry to thee, Mo - ther-

land, O mo-ther-land of mine. Sweet is thy beau - ty, Sweet is

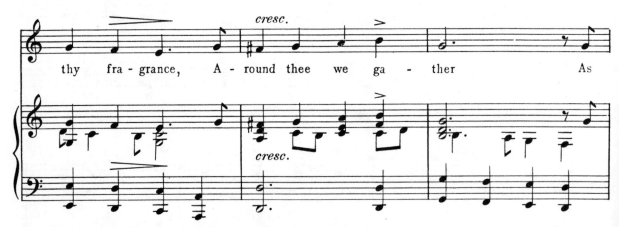

thy fra - grance, A - round thee we ga - ther As

This National Anthem, which was selected by means of a competition, came into use when Mauritius attained Independence on 12 March 1968.

It is played after the National Anthem for Great Britain when Her Majesty the Queen or her special representative (not including the Governor-General) is present, or when musical honours accompany the Royal Toast at a State Dinner.

one peo-ple, As one na-tion, For peace, jus-tice__ and li-ber-

ty._____ Be __ -lov __ -ed coun-try, may

God__ bless__ thee For e - ver and e - -ver.

MEXICO

Words by
FRANCISCO GONZÁLEZ BOCANEGRA
(1824-1861)
Translated by
Miss B. ROMERO
Versified by
J.E. HALES

Music by
JAIME NUNÓ
(1824-1908)

Words chosen from a government competition.
First performed 16th September, 1854, at the National Theatre in Mexico.

English words copyright J.B.Cramer & Co.Ltd.

- no - ro ru - gir del ca - ñón,_____ Y re-
Earth's deep foun-da - tions to trem - ble. Let the

-tiem - ble en sus cen - tros la tie - - rra al so-
guns with their thun - der ap - pal - - -ling Make the

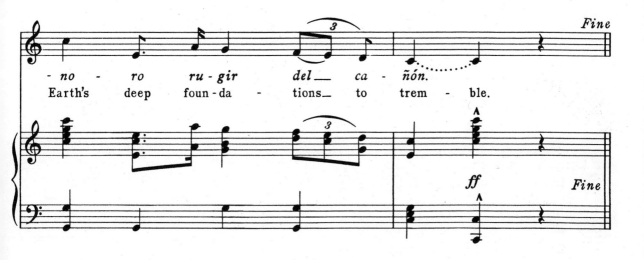

Fine

- no - ro ru - gir del__ ca - ñón.
Earth's deep foun-da - tions__ to trem - ble.

ff

Fine

Ci-ña ¡Oh pa - tria! tus sie - nes de o - li - - - va De la
May the an - gel di - vine, O dear Home - - - land, Crown thy

paz— el ar - cán - gel di - vi - - - no Que en el
brow— with the o - live— branch of peace; For thy

cie - lo tu e - ter - no des - ti - no Por el
des - ti - ny, traced by— God's own hand In the

de - - do de Dios se es - cri - bió Mas si o -
hea - - vens, shall e - ver in - crease. But should

-da-do en ca - da hi - jo te dió.
ev - 'ry___ one shall be found.

2. ¡Patria! ¡Patria! Tus hijos te juran
Exhalar en tus aras su aliento,
Si el clarín, con su bélico acento,
Los convoca a lidiar con valor.
¡Para ti las guirnaldas de oliva!
¡Un recuerdo para ellos de gloria!
¡Un laurel para ti de victoria!
¡Un sepulcro para ellos de honor!

CORO: Mexicanos, etc.

2. Blessed Homeland, thy children have vowed them
If the bugle to battle should call,
They will fight with the last breath allowed them
Till on thy loved altars they fall.
Let the garland of olive thine be;
Unto them be deathless fame;
Let the laurel of victory be assigned thee,
Enough for them the tomb's honoured name.

CHORUS: Mexicans, etc.

MONACO

French words by
LOUIS CANIS

Music by
BELLANDO DE CASTRO
Arr. by HENRY COLEMAN

1. Prin - ci - pau - té Mo - na - co ma pa - tri - e, Oh! com-bien Dieu est pro - di - gue pour toi. Ciel tou-jours pur, ri - ves tou - jours fleu - ri - es, Ton Sou - ve - rain est plus ai - mé qu'un

Performed for the first time in 1867

Roi. Ton Sou-ve-rain est plus ai-mé qu'un Roi.___

2. *Fiers Compagnons de la Garde Civique,*
   Respectons tous la voix du Commandant.
   Suivons toujours notre bannière antique.
   Le tambour bat, marchons tous en Avant. (bis)

3. *Oui, Monaco connut toujours des braves.*
   Nous sommes tous leurs dignes descendants.
   En aucun temps nous ne fûmes esclaves,
   Et loin de nous, régnèrent les tyrans. (bis)

4. *Que le nom d'un Prince plein de clémence*
   Soit repété par mille et mille chants.
   Nous mourons tous pour sa propre défense,
   Mais après nous, combattrons nos enfants. (bis)

1. Principality of Monaco, my country,
   Oh! how God is lavish with you.
   An ever-clear sky, ever-blossoming shores,
   Your Sovereign is better liked than a King. (repeat)

2. Proud Fellows of the Civic Guard,
   Let us all listen to the Commander's voice.
   Let us always follow our ancient flag.
   Drums are beating, let us all march forward. (repeat)

3. Yes, Monaco always had brave men.
   We all are their worthy descendants.
   We never were slaves,
   And far from us ruled the tyrants. (repeat)

4. Let the name of a Prince full of clemency
   Be repeated in thousands and thousands of songs.
   We shall all die in his defence,
   But after us, our children will fight. (repeat)

MONGOLIA

No words

It has not been possible to obtain any information about the history of this National Anthem.

MOROCCO
Hymne Cherifien

No words

This version conforms to the orchestration approved
by Si Mohammed Ben Youssef, Sultan of Morocco.
Arranged by LÉO MORGAN

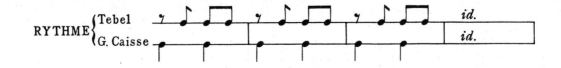

RYTHME { Tebel / G. Caisse

MUSCAT AND OMAN

Words by
RASHID BIN AZIZ (c. 1922)

This is sometimes played as a march. A transliterated
version of the words has been approximately fitted to the music.

-'id bil - tay - id   Wal 'izz al - ma - gid.   Wah -

-fadh lah - u   is - tiq - la - la - hu   Wa a -

D.C. al fine

-dim   'ala al-Is-lam   Dhilla li-wai-hi wal Mus-li-min.   ff

Translation

God save our Sultan Said;
Happy may he be with our support,
Honour and glory.
May his independence be preserved,
His banners perpetual giving their shade
Over Islam and Muslims.

NEPAL

NATIONAL ANTHEM FOR
H.M. THE MAHARAJA DHIRAJA

Shri mân gum - bhi - ra ne - pâ - li pra-chan-da pra-tâ- -pi bhu-pa-ti Shri pânch sar - kâr ma-hâ - râ- -jâ - dhi-râ - ja ko sa-dâ ra-hos un - na-ti Ra -

-khun chi râ - yu ee - sha - le pra - jâ phai -

- li - yos pu - kâ - raun ja - ya pre - ma - le Hâ -

-mi ne - pâ - li bhâ - ee sâ - râ - le.

Free Translation

May glory crown you, courageous Sovereign, you,
the gallant Nepalese,
Shri Pansh Maharajadhiraja, our glorious ruler.
May he live for many years to come and may the
number of his subjects increase.
Let every Nepalese sing this with joy.

NETHERLANDS
Wilhelmus van Nassouwe

Words by
MARNIX van St. ALDEGONDE
(1540-1598)
(Official Netherlands Government translation)

Composer unknown

1. *Wil - hel - mus van Nas - sou - we Ben ick van*
1. Wil - liam of Nas - sau,___ sci - on of Dutch and

Duit - schen bloet; Den Va - der - lant___ ghe -
an - cient line, I de - di - cate___ un -

-trou - we Blijf ick tot in___ den doet. Een___
-dy - ing faith to this land___ of mine. A___

Composer unknown: melody known from before 1572.
Song appeared in Valerius' "Gedenck-Clanck", 1626.
It has 15 verses in all.

prin - ce van O - ran - jen Ben ick
Prince am I, un - daunt - ed,___ of

vrij on - ver - veert; Den Co - ninck
O - range e'er free, To the King_____ of

van His - pan - jen Heb ick al - tijd ghe - eert.
Spain I've gran - ted a___ life's loy - al - ty.

2. *Mijn schilt en de betrouwen*
Sijt ghij, O Godt mijn Heer,
Op u soo wil ick bouwen
Verlaet mij nimmermeer!
Dat ick doch vroom mach blijven
U dienaer t'aller stondt,
Die Tyranny verdrijven,
Die mij mijn hert doorwondt.

2. My shield and my protection
Art Thou my Lord and God.
On Thee I build mine action,
Be evermore my rod.
That I be Thine eternal
And serve Thee fair and true
To chase tyrants infernal
Who my heart undo.

NETHERLANDS ANTILLES

Melody by
J. B. A. PALM
Harmonised by
F. H. van AANHOLT

There are at present no words to this National Anthem. The composer is the conductor of the Police Force Band, and this Band played it for the first time as a National Anthem on the second lustrum of the celebration of the Charter on 15 December 1964. It had been used in the past for some considerable time as the anthem of the island territory of Bonaire.

The Netherlands National Anthem, which is used with it, is usually played at the beginning of ceremonies and the Netherlands Antilles Anthem at the end.

NEWFOUNDLAND

Words by
CHARLES CAVENDISH BOYLE
(1849-1916)

Music by
C. H. PARRY
(1848-1918)
Arr. by HENRY COLEMAN

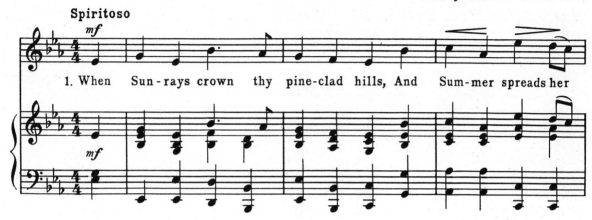

1. When Sun-rays crown thy pine-clad hills, And Sum-mer spreads her

hand, When sil-vern voi-ces tune thy rills We

love thee smil-ing land, We love thee, we

Sir Charles Cavendish Boyle wrote the words when he was Governor of Newfoundland. It was first performed in public 21st January 1902. Both this Anthem and that for Great Britain are used.

love thee, we love thee, smil - ing land.

2. When blinding storm-gusts fret thy shore,
    And wild waves lash thy strand,
    Thro' sprindrift swirl and tempest roar,
    We love thee, wind-swept land,
    We love thee, we love thee,
    We love thee, wind-swept land.

3. When spreads thy cloak of shimm'ring white,
    At Winter's stern command,
    Thro' shortened day and starlit night,
    We love thee, frozen land,
    We love thee, we love thee,
    We love thee, frozen land.

4. As loved our fathers, so we love,
    Where once they stood we stand,
    Their prayer we raise to heav'n above,
    God guard thee, Newfoundland,
    God guard thee, God guard thee,
    God guard thee, Newfoundland.

NEW ZEALAND
God Defend New Zealand

Words by
THOMAS BRACKEN (1843-1898)

Music by
JOHN J. WOODS (1849-1934)
Arr. by VERNON GRIFFITHS

By permission of the New Zealand Government, holders of the copyright.
This is New Zealand's National Song. The main anthem is that of Great Britain.

288

HIGH VOICES I (*prominent*)

2. Men of ev - 'ry creed and __ race Ga - ther here be - fore __ Thy __

HIGH VOICES II

2. Men of ev - 'ry creed and race Ga - ther here be - fore Thy __

LOW VOICES

2. Men of ev - 'ry creed and race Ga - ther here be - fore Thy

face, Ask - ing Thee to bless this place — God de - fend our Free -

face, Ask - ing Thee __ to __ bless this place — God de - fend our Free -

face, __ Ask - ing Thee to bless this place — God de - fend our Free -

land. From dis - sen-sion, en - vy, _ hate, And cor - rup - tion, guard our _

land. From dis - sen-sion, en - vy, hate, _ And cor - rup - tion, guard our

land. From dis - sen-sion, en - vy, hate, And cor - rup - tion, guard our

State; Make our coun-try good and great— God de - fend New Zea - land.

State; Make our coun-try_good and great_ God de - fend New Zea - land.

State; Make our coun-try good and_ great— God de - fend New Zea - land.

D.C. for v.3

NICARAGUA

Words by
SALOMÓN IBARRA MAYORGA
English versification by
MARY ELIZABETH SHAW

Composer unknown
(Composed before 1821)

The words formerly sung were replaced by these
words in 1939 by a governmental decree.

By permission of J.B.Cramer & Co.Ltd.

-ma - - nos tu glo - rio - so pen-dón__ bi-co-
proud - - ly, Stained with blood__ of thy chil - dren no

-lor,__ ni se ti - ñe con san - gre de her-ma-nos tu glo-
more, And thy ban - ner, twin-co - loured, flies proud-ly, Stained with

-rio - so pen-dón__ bi-co - lor. Bri - lle her-
blood of thy chil - dren no more. Gen - tle

-mo - sa la paz__ en tu cie - lo, na-da_em-pa - ñe tu
peace spreads her wings__ o'er thy coun-try, Whose fair glo - ry its

glo - ria in-mor-tal que_el tra - ba - jo_es tu dig - no lau-
pure - ness re - tains; For thy lau - rels by la - bour are

__ rel y el ho - nor_____ es tu en-se-ña tri-un-fal,_____
won. Ho-nour, un-dimmed,_____ thy shin-ing en - sign re - mains,_____

__ es tu en - se - ña tri - un - fal.
__ thy shin - ing en - sign re - mains.

NIGER
La Nigerienne

Words by MAURICE THIRIET

Music by
ROBERT JACQUET (b.1896)
NICK FRIONNET (b.1911)

1. Au - près du grand Ni - ger puis-sant   Qui rend la na-tu-re plus bel - le,

So - yons fiers et re - con - nais-sants   De no-tre li-ber-té nou - vel - le.

E - vi-tons les vai - nes que-rel - les   A-fin d'é-par - gner no-tre sang;

Et que les glo - rieux ac - cents De no-tre ra - ce sans tu -

- tel - le S'é - lèvent dans un même é - lan Jus -

- qu'à ce ciel é-blou-is-sant Où veil - le son âme é - ter -

- nel - le Qui fe - ra le pa-ys plus grand.___ De-

CHORUS

Allegro (2 in á bar)

-bout Ni-ger: De - bout!__ Que no - tre œu - vre fé - conde Ra-

-jeu - nis-se le cœur de ce vieux con - ti - nent__ Et

que ce chant s'en - tende__ aux qua - tre coins du mon - de Com-

-me le cri d'un Peuple é - qui-table et vail - lant!__ De-

-bout Ni-ger: De - bout!___ Sur le sol et sur l'on - de, Au

ryth-me des tam-tams, dans leur son gran-dis-sant, Res-

-tons u-nis, tou-jours,— et que cha-cun ré-pon - de A ce noble a - ve-

poco rall.

-nir qui nous dit "En___ a - vant."___

D. % Fine

T

2.   *Nous retrouvons dans nos enfants*
Toutes les vertus des Ancêtres:
Pour lutter dans tous les instants
Elles sont notre raison d'être.
Nous affrontons le fauve traître
A peine armés le plus souvent
Voulant subsister dignement
Sans detruire pour nous repaître.
Dans la steppe où chacun ressent
La soif, dans le Sahel brûlant,
Marchons, sans défaillance, en maîtres
Magnanimes et vigilants.

Translation by
T. M. CARTLEDGE

1.   By the waters of the mighty Niger
Which adds to the beauty of nature,
Let us be proud and grateful
For our new-won liberty.
Let us avoid vain quarrelling
So that our blood may be spared,
And may the glorious voice
Of our race, free from tutelage,
Rise unitedly, surging as from one man,
To the dazzling skies above
Where its eternal soul, watching over us,
Brings greatness to the country.

2.   We find again in our children
All the virtues of our ancestors.
Such virtues are our inspiration
For fighting at every moment.
We confront ferocious and treacherous animals
Often scarcely armed,
Seeking to live in dignity,
Not slaying with a lust to kill.
In the steppe where all feel thirst,
In the burning desert,
Let us march tirelessly forward
As magnanimous and vigilant masters.

Chorus
Arise, Niger, arise! May our fruitful work
Rejuvenate the heart of this old continent,
And may this song resound around the world
Like the cry of a just and valiant people.
Arise, Niger, arise! On land and river
To the rhythm of the swelling drum-beats' sound
May we ever be united and may each one of us
Answer the call of this noble future that says to us, "Forward!"

NIGERIA

Words by
LILIAN JEAN WILLIAMS

Music by
FRANCES BENDA

1. Ni - ger - i - a we hail thee, Our own dear na - tive land, Though
2. Our flag shall be a sym - bol That truth and jus - tice reign, In
3. O God of all cre - a - tion, Grant this our one re - quest, Help

tribe and tongue may dif - fer, In bro - ther - hood we stand, Ni -
peace or bat - tle hon - our'd, And this we count as gain, To
us to build a na - tion Where no man is op - pressed, And

- ger - ians all, and proud to serve Our sove reign Mo - ther - land.
hand on to our child - ren A ban - ner with - out stain.
so with peace and plen - ty Ni - ger - ia may be blessed.

The words and music were chosen as the result of a competition. It became
the National Anthem on 1st October, 1960, when Nigeria became independent.

NORWAY

Ja, vi elsker dette landet

Words by
BJÖRNSTERNE BJÖRNSSON
(1832-1910)
Translated by
G. M. GATHORNE-HARDY

Music by
RIKARD NORDRAAK
(1842-1866)

1. Ja, vi els - ker det - te lan - det,
1. Yes, we love with fond de - vo - tion

som det sti - ger frem, fu - ret, vær - bitt
This, the land that looms Rug - ged, storm-scarred,

o - ver van - net med de tu - sen hjem.
o'er the o - cean, With her thou - sand homes.

Adopted as the National Anthem in 1864, when first public recital
was given on the fiftieth anniversary of the Norwegian constitution.
Björnsson is one of Norway's great dramatists and poets.

Els - ker, els - ker det og ten - ker på vår far og
Love her, in our love re - call - ing Those who gave us

mor og den sa - ga - natt som sen - ker
birth, And old tales which night, in fall - ing,

dröm - me på vår jord, og den sa - ga - natt som
Brings as dreams to earth, And old tales which night, in

sen - ker, sen - ker dröm - me på vår jord!
fall - ing, Brings as dreams, as dreams to earth.

2. *Norske mann i hus og hytte,*
   takk din store Gud!
   Landet ville han beskytte,
   skjönt det mörkt så ut.
   Alt, hva fedrene har kjempet,
   mödrene har grett,
   har den Herre stille lempet,
   så vi vant vår rett,
   har den Herre stille lempet,
   så vi vant, vi vant vår rett.

3. *Ja, vi elsker dette landet,*
   som det stiger frem
   furet, værbitt over vannet,
   med de tusen hjem!
   Og som fedres kamp har hevet
   det av nöd til seir,
   også vi, når det blir krevet,
   for dets fred slår leir,
   ogsa vi, nar det blir krevet,
   for dets fred, dets fred slår leir!

2. Norseman, whatsoe'er thy station,
   Thank thy God, whose power
   Willed and wrought the land's salvation
   In her darkest hour.
   All our mothers sought with weeping
   And our sires in fight,
   God has fashioned, in his keeping, { bis. *(repeating "we gained"*
   Till we gained our right.   { *the second time)*

3. Yes, we love with fond devotion
   This our land that looms
   Rugged, storm-scarred, o'er the ocean
   With her thousand homes.
   And, as warrior sires have made her
   Wealth and fame increase,
   At the call we too will aid her, { bis. *(repeating "to guard"*
   Armed to guard her peace.   { *the second time)*

PAKISTAN

Words by
ABUL ASAR HAFEEZ JULLUNDURI

Music by
AHMAD G. CHAGLA
Arr. by BRYSON GERRARD

Moderato maestoso

Pak sar - zamin shad__ bad Kish-wa-ri haseen shad__ bad Tu - ni - sha - ni az - mi - a - li - -shan ar - zi Pak-is - tan Mar - ka-zi - yakin shad__ bad.

Music officially accepted as National Anthem of Pakistan, December 1953.
Words officially accepted as text of National Anthem of Pakistan, August 1954.

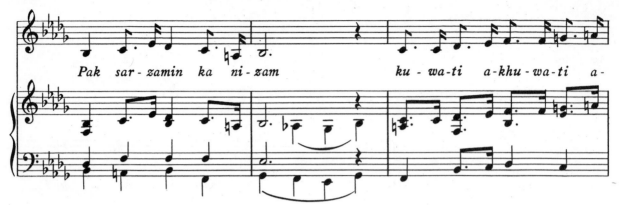

Pak sar - zamin ka ni - zam ... ku - wa - ti a - khu - wa - ti a-

-wam ... Kaum, mulk, Sul - tanat ... Pain - da ta bin-da bad

shad, bad___man zi - li mu - rad. ... Par-chami si-ta-ra-o hi-

-lal ... Rah - ba-ri tar-ra - ki-o ka mal

Tar - ju - ma - ni ma - zi - sha - ni hal ja - ni is - tik - bal

Say - yai, khu - dai zul ja - lal.

Free Translation

1.   Blessed be the sacred land,
     Happy be the beauteous realm,
     Symbol of high resolve,
     Land of Pakistan.
     Blessed be thou citadel of faith.

2.   The Order of this Sacred Land
     Is the might of the brotherhood of the people.
     May the nation, the country, and the State
     Shine in glory everlasting.
     Blessed be the goal of our ambition

3.   This flag of the Crescent and the Star
     Leads the way to progress and perfection,
     Interpreter of our past, glory of our present,
     Inspiration of our future,
     Symbol of Almighty's protection.

PANAMA

Words by
JERÓNIMO de la OSSA
(1847-1907)
English versification by
SEBASTIAN SHAW

Music by
SANTOS JORGE A.
(1870-1941)
Arr. by MARTIN SHAW

1. *Al - can - za - mos por fin la vic -*
1. Fi - nal vic - to - ry honoured then our

- to - ria, en el cam - po fe - liz de la u-nión,
sto - ry, When at last we gained u-nion's fair field.

Con ar -
Shin - ing

- dien - tes ful-go - res de glo - ria se ilu-
bright in the blaze of her glo - - ry, Now be -

This anthem was used for the first time on 4th November, 1903,
when the Panamanian people carried the flag of the new Republic
of Panama through the streets of the capital.

-mi - na la nue - va Na - ción_____ Con ar-dien-tes ful-go - res de
-hold, the new nation is re - vealed!_____ Shin-ing bright in the blaze of her

glo - ria se ilu-mi - na la nue - va Na - ción.
glo - ry, Now be-hold, the new nation is re - vealed!

Fine

VERSE
p dolce

Es pre-ci - so cu-brir con un ve - lo, del pa -
We re-joice that, the Cal - va - ry end - ed, And the

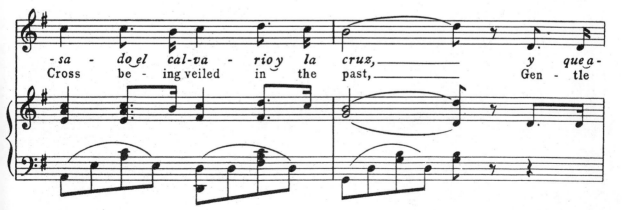

-sa - do el cal-va - rio y la cruz,_____ y que a-
Cross be - ing veiled in the past,_____ Gen - tle

-dor - ne el a - zul de tu ciel - - o, de con -
peace our blue skies has as - cend - - ed, Down in

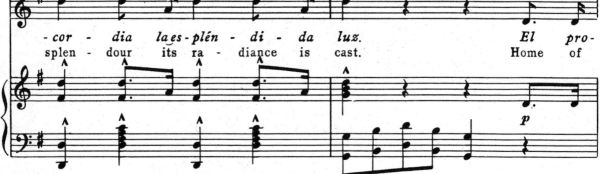

-cor - dia la es - plén - di - da luz. El pro-
splen - dour its ra - diance is cast. Home of

-gre - so a - ca - ri - cia tus la - - res, al com-
pro - gress, and blessed by en - dea - - vour, See, to

-pás de su - bli - me can - ción; ves ru-
mea - sure of mu - sic sub - lime, At your

-gir á tus pies am-bos ma - - - res, que dan
feet roar two o-ceans, which se - - - ver, For your

rum-bo a tu no-ble mi-sión.
mis - sion, a-way for all time.

D.S. 𝄋

2. *En tu suelo cubierto de flores,*
   A los besos del tibio terral,
   Terminaron guerreros fragores,
   Sólo reina el amor fraternal.
   Adelante la pica y la pala,
   Al trabajo sin más dilación:
   Y seremos asi prez y gala
   De este mundo feraz de Colón.

2. From your soil, where gay flowers are greeted
   By the warmth of the breezes' caress,
   Far the clamours of war have retreated;
   Love fraternal your future will bless.
   Then with spade and with hammer, untiring,
   To his task let each man set his hand;
   So, to honour and glory aspiring,
   Shall we prosper Columbus' fair land.

PARAGUAY

Words by
FRANCISCO ACUÑA de FIGUEROA (1790-1862)
Versified English version by
T. M. CARTLEDGE

Music by
FRANCISCO ACUÑA de FIGUEROA
Arr. by REMBERTO GIMENEZ (b. 1899)

Adopted as National Anthem, 1846
This present arrangement was declared the official version in May 1934.
Francisco Acuña de Figueroa also wrote the words of the Uruguayan Anthem

-do,   *Basta!...,   di* - *jo   y el   ce* - - *tro rom*-
-ing,   'Tis e - nough! they cried   and   broke   the pow-ers that had

-*pió.*   *Nue* - *stros   pa* -   *dres   li*-
reigned.   Our   fore - fa -   thers, mag-

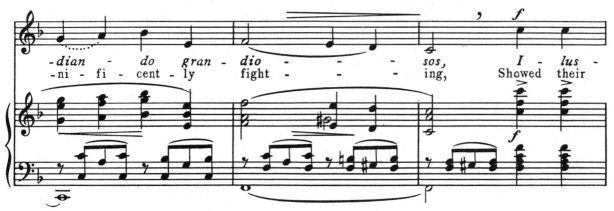

-*dian* - *do gran* - *dio* - - - *sos,*   *I - lus*-
-ni - fi - cent - ly   fight - - - ing,   Showed their

-*tra* - *ron su glo* - *ria mar* - *cial;*   *Y tro*-
mar - tial   glo - ry and pow'r;   And when

Allegro

-gua - yos, Re - pú - bli - ca o muer - te! Nue - stro
-guay - ans, Re - pub - lic or death we choose! 'Twas our

bri - o nos dió li - ber - tad; Ni o pre-
strength that gave us our fi - nal li - ber - ty. Nei - ther

-so - res, ni sier - vos, a - lien - tan, Don - de
ty - rants nor slaves can con - tin - ue, Where there

re - i - nan u - nión, é i - gual - dad. Ni o pre-
reign e - qual - i - ty and u - ni - ty. Nei - ther

U

-so - res, ni sier - vos, a - lien - tan, Don - de
ty - rants nor slaves can con - tin - ue Where there

re - i - nan u - nión, é i - gual - dad, u - nión, é i - gual -
reign e - qual - i - ty and u - ni - ty, where reign e - qual - i -

-dad, u - nión, é i - gual - dad. _____
-ty, and where reign u - ni - ty. _____

PERU

Words by
JOSÉ DE LA TORRE UGARTE
(1798-1878)

Music by
JOSÉ BERNARDO ALCEDO (1798-1878)
Arr. by HENRY COLEMAN

Marziale energico

CHORUS

So-mos li - bres, se - á - mos - lo

siem - pre, se - á - mos - lo siem - pre, y-an - tes nie - gue sus

lu - ces sus lu - ces sus lu - ces el sol, que fal -

Words and music chosen as result of a competition for a national anthem
promoted by General San Martin in 1821. Text (revised) declared
unalterable by a law which came into force 31st December, 1912.

-te - mos al vo - to so - lem - ne   que   la   Pa - tria al E - ter-no e-le-

-vó____   que fal - te-mos al vo - to so - lem - ne   que__ la

Pa - tria al E - ter - no e-le - vó____   que fal - te - mos al vo - to so-

-lem - ne   que__ la   Pa - tria al E - ter - no e-le - vó.____

VERSE

1. Lar - go tiem-po_el pe - rua - no_o-pri - mi - - do la_o - mi

- no - sa ca-de - na_arras-tró;____ con-de - na-do_a_u-na cruel ser-vi -

- dum - - bre, lar-go tiem-po lar-go tiem-po lar - go

tiem-po_en si-len - cio gi-mió.____ Mas a - pe-nas el gri - to sa-

-gra-do   ¡Li-ber-tad! en sus cos - tas___ se o - yó,   la in-do-

-len - cia de es-cla - vo sa - cu___ - de, la hu-mi-lla-do   la hu-mi-

-lla-do   la hu-mi - lla - do cerviz le - van - tó,_____ la hu-mi-

-lla - do cer-viz le-van - tó   cer-viz le - van - tó.___ So - mos

Free Translation

CHORUS   We are free; let us always be so,
          and let the sun rather deny its light
          than that we should fail the solemn vow
          which our Country raised to God.

VERSE   For a long time the Peruvian, oppressed,
          dragged the ominous chain;
          condemned to cruel serfdom,
          for a long time he moaned in silence.
          But as soon as the sacred cry of
          Freedom! was heard on his coasts
          he shakes the indolence of the slave,
          he raises his humiliated head.

NOTE: There were originally six verses, but
      this first verse only is now sung.

THE PHILIPPINES

Original Spanish words by
JOSÉ PALMA (1876-1903)
New Tagalog translation by
FELIPE P. DE LEON.
English trans. by M.A.L. Lane

Music by
JULIAN FELIPE (1861-1944)

Tagalog. Ba - yang ma - gi - liw, Per-las ng Si - la - nga - ṅan,
Land of the morn - ing, Child of the sun re - turn - ing,

A - lab ng pu - so Sa dib-dib mo'y bu - hay.
With fer - vour burn - ing Thee do our souls a - dore.

Lu - pang hi - ni - rang, Du - yan ka ng ma - gi - ting,
Land dear and ho - ly, Cra - dle of no - ble he - roes,

First performed in conjunction with the reading of the Act of
Proclamation of Philippine Independence, 12 June 1898.
The words were written in 1899.

Fine

Sa man - lu - lu - pig Di ka pa - si - si - il.
Ne'er shall in - va - ders Tram-ple thy sa - cred shore.

Sa da - gat at bun - dok, Sa si - moy at sa
Ev - er with - in thy skies and through thy clouds And

la - ngit mong bug - haw, May di - lag ang tu - la At
o'er thy hills and sea Do we be - hold the ra - diance,

a - wit sa pag - la - yang mi - na - ma -
Feel the throb, Of glo - rious lib - er -

la - ngit sa pi - ling mo;_____ A - ming li -
-brace 'tis rap - ture to lie;_____ But it is

-ga - ya, na pag ma'y mang - a - a - pi, Ang ma - ma -
glo - ry ev - er, When thou__ art__ wronged For us, thy

-tay nang da - hil sa iyo._____
sons, to suf - fer and die._____

D.C. al Fine

D.C. al Fine

Ped.

THE PHILIPPINES
Original words written in Spanish

Tierra adorada.
hija del sol de Oriente
su fuego ardiente
en ti latiendo esta.

Tierra de amores,
del heroismo cuna,
los invasores
no te hollaran jamas.

En tu azul cielo, en tus auras,
en tus montes y en tu mar
esplende y late el poema
de tu amada libertad.

Tu pabellon que en las lides
la victoria ilumino
no veranunca apagados
sus estrellas ni su sol.

Tierra de dichas, de sol y amores,
en tu regazo dulce es vivir;
es una gloria para tus hijos,
cuando te ofenden, por ti morir.

POLAND

Words by
General JOSEF WYBICKI
(1747-1822)

Translated by
MARTIN SHAW

Music: Traditional

Allegretto vivace

1. Jeszc - ze Pol - ska   nie zgi - ng - ta,__ kie - dy my   zy -
1. Po - land still   is   ours for ev - er,__ Long as Poles   re -

-je - my,   co nam ob - ca   prze - moc wzię - ła,__
-main;__   Chains the foe   bound   on her nev - er__

szab - lą od - bie - rze - my.   Marsz, marsz, Dą - brow - ski;
Shall the foe   re - tain.__   On!   On!   Da - bru - ski!*   from

This song, first sung in 1795, was a favourite with the Polish
Legions in the Napoleonic wars. It has been sung all over
Poland since 1912; in 1927 it was authorized as its National
Anthem by the new Polish republican government.
*General Dabruski (1755-1818) commanded the Polish Legions.
General Wybicki was among those who organised and led the Legions.
He was also a poet and a member of the Polish Parliament.

z zie - mi wło - skiej do Pol - ski! Za two-im prze -
I - ta-ly's ___ fair - plain! ___ Lead us on to

- *wo - dem złac - zym się zna - ro - dem.*
greet our home - land, Lead us back a - gain! ___

2. *Przejdziem Wislę, przejdziem Wartę,*
   będziem Polakami,
   dał nam przykład Bonaparte
   jak zwyciężać mamy.
   Marsz, marsz, Dąbrowski

3. *Jak Czarniecki do Poznania*
   po szwedzkim zaborze,
   dla ojczyzny ratowania
   wrócim się przez morze.
   Marsz, marsz, Dąbrowski

2. Vistula and Wartar over,
   Poles we'll ever be;
   And from Bonaparte discover
   Paths to victory.
   On! On! etc.

3. When the Swede had forged our chain,
   The Fatherland to save,
   Czarniecki, Poznan town to gain,
   Plunged into the wave.
   On! On! etc.

PORTUGAL

Words by
HENRIQUE LOPES DE MENDONÇA (1856-1931)

Music by
ALFREDO KEIL
(1850-1907)
Arr. by HENRY COLEMAN

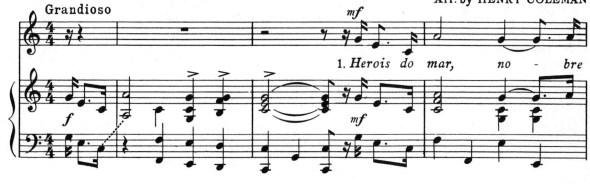

1. Herois do mar, no - bre

po - vo, Na - ção va - len - te,____ i - mor - tal, Le - van-

-tai ho - je de no - vo O es-plen - dor____ de Por - tu-

gal!____ En - tre as bru - mas da me - mó - ria, Ó

First played January 1890, approved as the National Anthem in 1910.

Pá - tria, sen - te - se a voz___ Dos teus e - gré - gios a-

vós, Que há - de gui-ar - te à vi - tó - ri-a! Às

ar - mas! Às ar - mas! So-bre a ter - ra, so - bre o

CHORUS

mar___ Às ar - mas! Às ar - mas! Pe - la

Pá - tria lu - tar!____Con-tra os ca-nhões mar-char, mar-char!

2. Desfralda a invicta bandeira
À luz viva do teu céu!
Brade à Europa à terra inteira:
Portugal não pereceu!
Beija o solo teu jucundo
O Oceano a rugir d'amor;
E o teu braço vencedor
Deu novos mundos ao mundo!

Às armas, às armas!
Sobre a terra, sobre o mar,
Às armas, às armas!
Pela pátria lutar!
Contra os canhões marchar,
    Marchar!

3. Saudai o sol que desponta
Sobre um ridente porvir;
Seja o eco de uma afronta
O sinal do ressurgir.
Ráios dessa aurora forte
São como beijos de mãe
Que nos guardam, nos sustêm
Contra as injúrias da sorte.

Às armas, às armas!
Sobre a terra, sobre o mar,
Às armas, às armas!
Pela pátria lutar!
Contra os canhões marchar,
    Marchar!

1.   Heroes of the sea, noble race
valiant and immortal nation,
now is the hour to raise up on high once more
Portugal's splendour.
From out of the mists of memory,
oh Homeland, we hear the voices
of your great forefathers
that shall lead you on to victory!

CHORUS

To arms, to arms
on land and sea!
To arms, to arms
to fight for our Homeland!
To march against the enemy guns!

2.   Unfurl the unconquerable flag
in the bright light of your sky!
Cry out to all Europe and the whole world
that Portugal has not perished.
Your happy land is kissed
by the Ocean that murmurs with love.
And your conquering arm
has given new worlds to the world!

CHORUS

To arms, to arms
on land and sea!
To arms, to arms
to fight for our Homeland!
To march against the enemy guns!

3.   Salute the Sun that rises
on a smiling future:
let the echo of an insult be
the signal for our revival.
The rays of that powerful dawn
are like a mother's kisses
that protect us and support us
against the insults of fate.

CHORUS

To arms, to arms
on land and sea!
To arms, to arms
to fight for our Homeland!
To march against the enemy guns!

PUERTO RICO

La Borinqueña

Music by F. ASTOL
Arranged by RAMÓN COLLADO

This anthem was designated as the Anthem of Puerto Rico in 1952. It has no official words.
Its use is governed by a Regulation promulgated by the Secretary of State of Puerto Rico
on May 2nd 1960, according to Act Nº 2 of the Legislative Assembly of 24th July 1952.
The Puerto Ricans, being American citizens, also use the anthem of the U.S.A.

QATAR

ROMANIA
Trăiască Regele

Words by
VASILE ALECSANDRI

Music by
EDWARD A. HÜBSCH (1813-1894)
Arr. by **HENRY COLEMAN**

Allegro maestoso

Tră - ias - că Re - ge - le În pa - ce şi o - nor, De ţa - ră iu - bi - tor Şi-a - pă - ră - tor de ţa - ră!

This National Anthem of Romania (which was proclaimed a kingdom on 10th May, 1881) is at present not sung inside Romania as the anthem which follows has officially replaced it.

Fi - e Domn glo - ri - os ____ Pes - te -

- noi, Fi - e'n veci no - ro -

- cos ____ În ____ răz - boi!

O! Doam - ne ____ Sfin - te, Ce - resc Pă -

-rin - te, Sus - ti - ne cu - a ta

mâ - nă Co-roa - na Ro-mâ - nă! -nă!

2.   *Traiască Patria*
    Cât soarele ceresc,
    Rai dulce, românesc,
    Ce poartă-un mare nume!
      Fie'n veci el ferit
      De nevoi!
      Fie'n veci locuit
      De eroi!
    O! Doamne Sfinte,
    Ceresc Părinte
    Întinde-a ta mână
    Pe țara română!

1. Long live our King
    In peace and honour,
    Loving his country
    Defending our fatherland!
      Let him be glorious
      Rule over us,
      Always victorious
      In war.
    O Lord the Holy,
    Our heavenly Father,
    Support with thy hands
    The Romanian Crown!
	2. Long live our fatherland
	    As long as the sun,
	    Sweet paradise
	    With glorious name!
	      Let it always be free
	      Of worries!
	      Let it always be inhabited
	      By heroes!
	    O Lord the Holy
	    Our heavenly Father,
	    Protect with thy hand
	    The Romanian land!

Pronunciation:

ă like er in "father"	ce as che
Î like u in "une" in French	Și-a as sha
e (throughout) as in "get"	veci as vech
ț as ts	ge as in gentle

ROMANIA

Words by
EUGEN FRUNZA and DAN DESLIU

Music by
MATEI SOCOR

1. Te slă - vim, Ro - mâ - ni - e, pă - mânt pă - rin-tesc, Mân - dre pla - iuri sub ce - rul tău pas - nic ro-desc. E zdro - bit al tre - cu - tu - lui

2. (In - fră) - ţit fi - va ves - nic al nos - tru po - por Cu po - po - rul so - vie - tic e - li - be - ra-tor. Le - ni - nis - mul ni-e far, şi tă -

3. (Noi u) - zi - ne clă - dim, ro - dul hol - dei spo-rim, Vrem în pa - ce cu ori - ce po - por să tră - im. Dar dus - ma - nii de-ar fi să ne

This officially became the National Anthem in 1953

jug bles - te - mat, Nu za - dar - nic strā - bu - nii e -
-ri - e si-a-vânt, Noi ur - măm cu cre - din - ță Par -
cal - ce în prag, Îi vom frân - ge în nu - me-le-a

-roi au lup - tat, As - tāzi noi___ îm - pli - nim vi - sul
-ti - dul ne'n-frânt, Fa - u - rim___ so - cia - lis - mul pe-al
tot ce ni-e drag. Î năl - ta___ vom spre glo - rie al

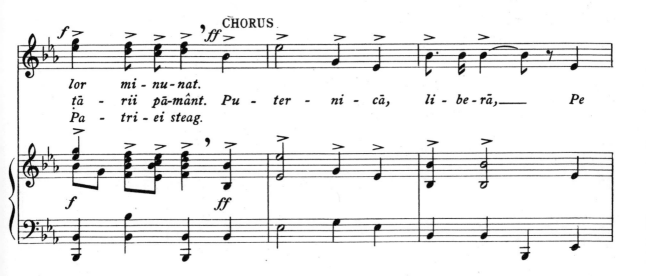

CHORUS

lor mi - nu - nat.
tā - rii pā-mânt. Pu - ter - ni - cā, li - be - rā,___ Pe
Pa - tri - ei steag.

soar___ tă stă - pâ - nă, Tră - ias___ că Re -

-pu - bli - ca Po - pu - la - ră Ro -

-mâ - nă! Tra - ias - că Re - pu - bli - ca___ Po - pu-

-la - ră Ro - mâ - nă! 2. În - fră - mâ - nă!
3. Noi u -

1. We glorify thee, Romania, soil of our parents,
   Fine orchards are bearing fruit under thy peaceful sky,
   The accursed yoke of the past is smashed,
   Not in vain have fought our ancestral heroes,
   Nowadays we are carrying out their wonderful dream.

   Chorus: Strong, free,
   Mistress of thy fate
   Long live the Romanian
   Popular Republic!

2. May our nation be always fraternal
   With the Soviet people, our liberators.
   Leninism is our guiding light, our strength and our enthusiasm,
   We follow with faith the unvanquished party,
   We are creating socialism on our Country's soil.

3. We are building new factories, we are increasing the yield of the harvest,
   We want to live in peace with any nation,
   But should the foes cross our threshold,
   We shall break them in the name of all that is dear to us
   And shall raise towards glory the flag of our Fatherland

RWANDA

Rwanda rwacu

Based on an old Rwandan Folk tune by a
group of Rwandans 'Abanyuramatwi'
Arranged by W. L. REED

Moderato maestoso

1. Rwa - nda rwa-cu, Rwa-nda gi-hu-gu cya-mbya-ye,
2. I - mpu-ndu ni zi-vu-ge mu Rwa-nda ho - se:
3. Ba - vu-ka Rwa-nda mwe-se mu-vu z'i-mpu-ndu,
4. Ni - mu-cyo du-si-ngi-z'I-be-nde-ra rya-cu.

con 8va ad lib.

nda - ku - ra - ta - n'i - shya - ka n'u - bu - twa - li.
Re - pu - bu - li - ka ya-ku y'u - bu - ha - ke,
De - mo - ka - ra - si ya-rwo i - ra - ga - nje.
A - ra - ka - ba - ho na Pre - zi - da wa - cu.

I - yo ni - bu-ts'i - bi gwi wa-gi - ze ku - ge-z̆u-bu,
u - bu - ko - lo - ni - ze bwa-gi-ye nk'i - fu - n'i-he - ze.
Twa - yi - ha - ra - ni - ye rwo-se twe-s'u - ko tu-nga-na.
Ba - ra - ka - ba-hw'a-ba-tu-ra-ge b'i - ki Gi-hu-gu.

This anthem was adopted by the National Assembly
and sanctioned by the President of the Republic on
11th December 1962, the year when **Rwanda** became
independent.

nshi - mi - ra A - ba-rwa - na-shya - ka ba-za-nye Re - pu-bu - li - ka
Shi - ng'u - mu-zi De-mo - ka - ra - si wa-du-ha - ye kwi-to - re - ra
Ga - tu - tsi, Ga-twa na ga-hu - tu na-mwe ba - nya-rwa-nda ba-ndi
I - nte - go ya-cu Ba - nya-rwa-nda twi-shyi - re ka-ndi twi-za - ne

i - da - hi-nyu-ka. Ba - va-ndi-mwe___ b'u - ru Rwa-nda
a - ba-te-ge-tsi. Ba-nya-rwa-nda:___ a - ba-ku - ru
mwa-byi-ye-me-je, I - nde-pa-nda - nsi twa-tsi-ndi-ye___
mu Rwa-nda rwa-cu. Twe-se ha-mwe,___ twu-ng'u-bu-mwe

rwa-cu twe-se___ ni - mu-ha-gu-ru-ke: Tu - ru-bu-mba-ti - re mu ma-
na-mw'a-ba-to___ mwi-zi-hi-y'u Rwa-nda: Tu - ru-bu-mba-ti - re mu ma-
twe-se ha-mwe___ tu - yi-shyi-gi-ki - re: Tu - yi-bu-mba-ti - re mu ma-
nta mu-su-su___ du - te - r'i-mbe-re ko: Tu - ru-bu-mba-ti - re mu ma-

ho - ro, mu ku - li, mu bwi - ge - nge no mu bwu - mvi - ka - ne.
ho - ro, mu ku - li, mu bwi - ge - nge no mu bwu - mvi - ka - ne.
ho - ro, mu ku - li, mu bwi - ge - nge no mu bwu - mvi - ka - ne.
ho - ro, mu ku - li, mu bwi - ge - nge no mu bwu - mvi - ka - ne.

1. My Rwanda, land that gave me birth,
    Fearlessly, tirelessly, I boast of you!
    When I recall your achievements to this very day,
    I praise the pioneers who have brought in our unshakeable Republic.
    Brothers all, sons of this Rwanda of ours,
    Come rise up all of you,
            Let us cherish her in peace and in truth,
            In freedom and in harmony!

2. Let the victory drums beat throughout all Rwanda!
    The Republic has swept away feudal bondage.
    Colonialism has faded away like a worn-out shoe.
    Democracy take root!
    Through you we have chosen our own rulers.
    People of Rwanda, old and young, citizens all,
            Let us cherish her in peace and in truth,
            In freedom and in harmony!

3. Home-born Rwandans all, beat the victory drums!
    Democracy has triumphed in our land.
    All of us together we have striven for it arduously.
    Together we have decreed it—Tutsi, Twa, Hutu, with other racial elements,
    This hard-won Independence of ours,
    Let us all join to build it up!
            Let us cherish it in peace and in truth,
            In freedom and in harmony!

4. Come let us extol our Flag!
    Long live our President, long live the citizens of our land!
    Let this be our aim, people of Rwanda:
    To stand on our own feet, in our own right, by our own means.
    Let us promote unity and banish fear.
    Let us go forward together in Rwanda.
            Let us cherish her in peace and in truth,
            In freedom and in harmony!

SABAH

Words and Music by
H. B. HERMANN

Sa - bah ta - nah ay - er ku, _____ Ne - ge -
Sa - bah my_ mo - ther - land, _____ Our_

ri ki - ta yang ter-chin - ta, _____ Pe - mu - da, Pe - mu - di se - mu -
most be - loved home - land, _____ Come all young men and_

a ma-ri lah Ba-ngun lah ber-sa - tu se-mu - a, _____ Ma - ri
wo - men a-rise, Let us all u - nite to - ge - - ther. Come

SAN MARINO

Words by
GIOSUÈ CARDUCCI

Music by
FEDERICO CONSOLO
(1841-1906)

O - no - re a te o - no - re o an - ti - ca Re-

-pu - bli - ca vir - tuo - - sa - tuo - - sa

-ge - ne - ro - sa fi - den - te o - no - re a

Y

Free Translation

Honour to you, O ancient Republic,
Virtuous, generous, faithful!
Honour to you, and live eternally
Within the life and the glory of Italy.

SAUDI ARABIA

Music by
A.R. AL-HATIB

No words

First performed 1947, adopted 1950.

SENEGAL

Words by
LEOPOLD SÉDAR SENGHOR (b.1906)

Music by
HERBERT PEPPER

1. Pin - cez tous vos Ko - ras, Frap-pez les ba - la - fons, Le

Lion rouge a ru - gi Le Domp-teur de la brousse d'un

bond s'est é - lan - cé Dis - si - pant les tén - è - bres. So -

Senegal became independent on 4th April 1960
This National Anthem was adopted in 1960
The words are by the President, Leopold Sédar Senghor

*Harp-Lute of the Senegalese Griots.

-leil sur nos ter-reurs, So - leil sur nos es-poirs.____

De-bout frè - res voi - ci l'A-fri-que ras-sem-blé - e.

CHORUS

Fi - bres de mon coeur vert, E-pau-le contre é-pau-le,

Mes plus que frères O Sé - né - ga-lais, de - bout!____

U-nis-sons la mer et les sour-ces, U-nis-sons la

steppe et la fo-rêt. Sa-lut Af-ri-que mè-re. -lut A-fri-que mère.

2. *Sénégal, toi le fils de l'écume du Lion,*
   Toi surgi de la nuit au galop des chevaux,
   Rends-nous, oh! rends-nous l'honneur de nos Ancêtres,
   Splendides comme ébène et forts comme le muscle
   Nous disons droits— l'épée n'a pas une bavure.

3. *Sénégal, nous faisons nôtre ton grand dessein:*
   Rassembler les poussins à l'abri des milans
   Pour en faire, de l'Est à l'Ouest, du Nord au Sud,
   Dressé, un même peuple, un peuple sans couture
   Mais un peuple tourné vers tous les vents du monde.

4. *Sénégal, comme toi, comme tous nos héros,*
   Nous serons durs sans haine et des deux bras ouverts.
   L'épée, nous la mettrons dans la paix du fourreau,
   Car le travail sera notre arme et la parole.
   Le Bantou est un frère, et l'Arabe et le Blanc.

5. *Mais que si l'ennemi incendie nos frontières*
Nous serons tous dressés et les armes au poing:
Un Peuple dans sa foi défiant tous les malheurs,
Les jeunes et les vieux, les hommes et les femmes.
La Mort, oui! Nous disons la Mort, mais pas la honte.

Free Translation by
ELIZABETH P. COLEMAN

1. Sound, all of you, your Koras,
Beat the drums,
The red Lion has roared,
The Tamer of the bush with one leap has rushed forward
Scattering the gloom.
Light on our terrors,
Light on our hopes.
Arise, brothers, Africa behold united.

Chorus

Shoulder to shoulder,
O people of Senegal, more than brothers to me, arise!
Unite the sea and the springs,
Unite the steppe and the forest.
Hail, mother Africa,
Hail, mother Africa.

2. Senegal, thou son of the Lion,
Arise in the night with great speed,
Restore, oh, restore to us the honour of our ancestors,
Magnificent as ebony and strong as muscles,
We are a straight people—the sword has no fault.

3. Senegal, we make your great design our own:
To gather the chicks, sheltering them from kites,
To make from them, from East to West, from North to South,
A people rising as one, in seamless unity,
Yet a people facing all the winds of the earth.

4. Senegal, like thee, like all our heroes,
We will be stern without hatred, and with open arms.
The sword we will put peacefully in its sheath,
For work and words will be our weapon.
The Bantu is our brother, the Arab, and the White man too.

5. But if the enemy violates our frontiers,
We will all be ready, weapons in our hands;
A people in its faith defying all evil;
Young and old, men and women,
Death, yes! but not dishonour.

SIERRA LEONE

Words by
C. N. FYLE

Music by JOHN J. AKAR
Arr. by HENRY COLEMAN

1. High we ex-alt thee, realm of the free; Great is the love we have for thee; Firm-ly u-nit-ed e-ver we stand, Sing-ing thy praise, O native land. We raise up our hearts and our

Written and composed in 1961 and adopted as the National Anthem
when Sierra Leone achieved independence on 27th April 1961
Both author and composer are Sierra Leonians; C.N. Fyle being a tutor at a
boys' high school, and John J. Akar Director of the Sierre Leone Broadcasting Service.

voic - es on high, the hills and the val - leys re - e - cho our cry;

Bless-ing and peace be e - ver thine own, Land that we love, our_ Sier - ra Le-one.

2. One with a faith that wisdom inspires,
   One with a zeal that never tires;
   Ever we seek to honour thy name,
   Ours is the labour, thine the fame.
   We pray that no harm on thy children may fall,
   That blessing and peace may descend on us all;
   So may we serve thee ever alone,
   Land that we love, our Sierra Leone.

3. Knowledge and truth our forefathers spread,
   Mighty the nations whom they led;
   Mighty they made thee, so too may we
   Show forth the good that is ever in thee.
   We pledge our devotion, our strength and our might,
   Thy cause to defend and to stand for thy right;
   All that we have be ever thine own,
   Land that we love, our Sierra Leone.

SINGAPORE
Majulah Singapura

Words and Music by
ZUBIR SAID
Arr. by HENRY COLEMAN

Ma-ri ki - ta ra'- yat Si - nga - pu - ra sa - ma sa - ma mĕ - nu - ju ba - ha - gi - a. Chi - ta chi - ta ki - ta yang mu - li - a Ber - ja - ya Si - nga - pu - ra!

For Royal Salute play from ★ to ★

First performed September, 1958. It became very popular and when
Singapore became self-governing on 3rd June 1959 it was decided to
make it the National Anthem. It was officially adopted as such
by the Legislative Assembly of Singapore on 30th November, 1959.

Ma-ri-lah ki-ta ber-sa-tu,____ De ngan sĕ-ma-ngat yang ba-

-ru.____ Sĕ-mu-a ki-ta ber-se-ru Ma-ju-lah__ Si-nga-pu-

-ra, Ma-ju-lah__ Si-nga-pu-ra! Ma-ri-____ra!

Free Translation

Let us, the people of Singapore, together march
forward towards happiness. Our noble aspiration
is to see Singapore achieve success.
Let us unite in a new spirit. We all pray:
"May Singapore Progress", "May Singapore Progress".

SOMALIA

Music, traditional.
Transcribed by R.A.Y. MITCHELL
Piano arr. by HENRY COLEMAN

This traditional music was adopted as the National Anthem when Somaliland
became independent on 26 June, 1960. It was recorded by village musicians
and transcribed by R.A.Y. Mitchell, Bandmaster of the Military Band of The
Royal Highland Fusiliers, who performed it at Independence Celebrations

SOUTH AFRICA

Die Stem van Suid-Afrika
THE CALL OF SOUTH AFRICA

Words by
C.J. LANGENHOVEN, 1918
Official English translation, 1952, amended 1959

Music by
M.L. de VILLIERS, 1921

1. *Uit die blou van on se he - mel, uit die diep - te van ons*
2. *In die merg van ons ge - been - te, in ons hart en siel en*

1. Ring-ing out from our blue hea - vens, from our deep seas break-ing
2. In our bo - dy and our spi - rit, in our in - most heart held

see, *Oor ons e - wi - ge ge - berg - tes waar die*
gees, *In ons roem op ons ver - le - de, in ons*
round; O - ver e - ver - last - ing moun - tains where the
fast; In the prom - ise of our fu - ture and the

with emphasis

kran - se__ ant - woord gee,   *Deur ons vér ver - la - te*
hoop op__ wat sal wees,   *In ons wil en werk en*
e - choing crags re - sound;   From our plains where creak - ing
glo - ry__ of our past;   In our will, our work, our

a tempo

vlak - tes met die kreun van os - se - wa__   *Ruis die*
wan - del, van ons wieg tot aan ons graf__   *Deel geen*
wag - ons cut their trails in - to the earth__   Calls the
striv - ing, from the cra - dle to the grave__   There's no

stem van ons ge - lief - de, van ons land Suid - A - fri -
an - der land ons lief - de, trek geen an - der__ trou ons
spi - rit of our Coun - try, of the land that__ gave us
land that shares our lov - ing, and no bond that__ can en -

3 *In die songloed van ons somer, in ons winternag se kou,*
    In die lente van ons liefde, in die lanfer van ons rou,
    By die klink van huŵliks-klokkies, by die kluitklap op die kis—
    Streel jou stem ons nooit verniet nie, weet jy waar jou kinders is.
    Op jou roep sê ons nooit nee nie, sê ons altyd, altyd ja:
    Om te lewe, on te sterwe-ja, ons kom, Suid-Afrika.

4 *Op U Almag vas vertrouend het ons vadere gebou:*
    Skenk ook ons die krag, o Here! om te handhaaf en te hou—
    Dat die erwe van ons vaad're vir ons kinders erwe bly:
    Knegte van die Allerhoogste, teen die hele wêreld vry.
    Soos ons vadere vertrou het, leer ook ons vertrou, o Heer—
    Met ons land en met ons nasie sal dit wel wees, God regeer.

3 In the golden warmth of summer, in the chill of winter's air,
    In the surging life of springtime, in the autumn of despair;
    When the wedding bells are chiming or when those we love depart,
    Thou dost know us for thy children and dost take us to thy heart.
    Loudly peals the answering chorus: We are thine, and we shall stand,
    Be it life or death, to answer to thy call, beloved land.

4 In thy power, Almighty, trusting, did our fathers build of old;
    Strengthen then, O Lord, their children to defend, to love, to hold —
    That the heritage they gave us for our children yet may be:
    Bondsmen only to the Highest and before the whole world free.
    As our fathers trusted humbly, teach us, Lord, to trust Thee still:
    Guard our land and guide our people in Thy way to do Thy will.

SOUTHERN YEMEN

No words

Music by
JUMA'A KHAN
Arranged by W. L. REED

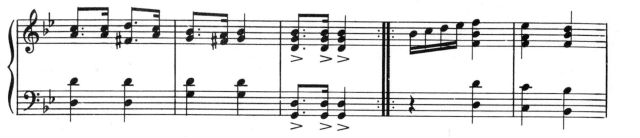

First used on the occasion of the Independence of the
People's Republic of Southern Yemen, 30 November 1967.

z

SPAIN

18th-Century tune
Orchestrated by
BARTOLOMÉ PÉREZ CASAS (b.1873)
Arr. by MARTIN SHAW

Marziale marcato e sostenuto

This anthem, the *Marcha Real*, dates from 3rd September, 1770, when
it was declared by Royal Decree of Carlos III as the Spanish Royal March.
In July 1942 General Franco issued a decree declaring it as the national
hymn. There are no official words, though various writers have written
verses at different times.

SUDAN

Words by
AHMED MOHAMED SALIH
English versification by
T. M. CARTLEDGE

Music by
Captain MURGAN
Arr. by T. M. CARTLEDGE

NAH-NU DJUN-DUL-LÂH DJUN-DUL-WA-TAN.
We are the ar-my of God and of our land,

IN___ DÂ 'Â DÂ 'IL FI-DÂ LÄM NA-KhUN.
We shall ne-ver fail, called to make sac-ri-fice.

NÄ-TÄ-HAD-DAL MAUT 'END-ÄL-MI-HAN.
Wheth-er brav-ing death, hard-ship or pain,

NÄSh - TÄ RIL — MÄDJD BI ÄGh - LÄ - ThÄ-MÄN.
We for glo - ry give our lives as the price.

HÄ - ThI-HIL ARD LÄ-NÄ! FÄL - YÄ-'ISh SÛ - DÄ - NU-NÄ,
This our land, our Su-dan, Long may she now live, we pray,

'A - LA-MAN BÄYN ÄL U - MÄM.
Show-ing all na - tions the way.

YÄ BE-NIS-SÚ-DẪN, HÄ-ThÄRAM-ZU-KUM:
Sons of the Su - dan, sum - moned now to serve.

YAH MI-LUL-'EB, WÄ YAH-MÎ AR-DA-KUM.
Shoul - der-ing the task our coun - try to pre - serve.

Key to phonetic transliteration of Arabic text

^ for long vowels

Û as *oo* in *pool*

U nearer *u* in *put*

Ä as *a* in *cat*

A as *a* in *rather*

ÀYN approx. as *ine* in *fine*

Th ① as *th* in *thing*

Th ② as *th* in *this*

Ḥ aspirated at back of mouth

Kh like hard *ch* in German *Buch*

Gh like gutteral *r* in French *rang*

' like last *a* of *China*

AUT like *out*

SURINAM

Words by
C. A. HOEKSTRA (1893)

Music by
C. de PUY (1876)
Arr. by HENRY COLEMAN

Moderato

Su - ri - na - me's trot - se stro - men, Su - ri -
God zij met ons Su - ri - na - me! Hij ver -

- na - me's heer - lijk land, Su - ri - na - me's fie - re
- heff' ons heer - lijk land! Doch dat elk zich dan ook

bo - men, Trouw zijn wij aan u ver - pand. Moch-ten weer de vlo - ten
scha - me, Die zijn e - re maakt ten schand. Recht en waar-heid te be -

Surinam uses the Netherlands National Anthem, and
the above National Anthem is played after that.

va - - ren, Dat de han - del we - lig bloei, Dat fa-
-trach - - ten, Zeed'-lijk rein en vroom en vrij, Al wat

- brie - ken wel-vaart ba - - ren, Dat hier al - les we - lig_ groei!
slecht is te ver - ach - ten, Dat geeft aan ons land waar - dij!

Free Translation

Proud streams of Surinam,
Beautiful land of Surinam,
Stately trees of Surinam,
In faith we are pledged to you.
May the fleets sail again,
And the trade flourish,
May the factories bring prosperity
And may everything thrive!

God will be with our Surinam!
May He glorify our beautiful land!
But he who makes of his honour a disgrace,
Must then be filled with shame.
Try to be upright and truthful,
Morally pure, devout and joyful,
And despise everything which is bad;
This will make our country a worthy land!

SWAZILAND

Words by
Mrs. A.F.K. SIMELANE

Music by
DAVID RYCROFT

This anthem was selected from some 100 entries in a National Anthem
competition, when Swaziland attained independence on 6th September 1968.
The composer, Mr. David Rycroft, is a Lecturer in Bantu Languages at the
University of London, and author of the first Swazi-English dictionary.
His anthem was composed after ethnomusicological fieldwork in Swaziland
and is a compromise between Swazi and Western music. The Swazi musical
tradition is unusual in that there are no drums. The stress is on choral dance-
songs, with intricate polyphony, rather than on the more usual rhythmic subtle-
ties found elsewhere in Africa.

This piano arrangement © 1969 David Rycroft

fu - la; Bu - si - sa ti - pha-tshi - ma - ndla taka -

fu - la; Bu - si - sa ti - pha-tshi - ma - ndla taka -
fu - la; Bu - si - sa ti - pha-tshi - ma - ndla taka -

fu - la; Bu - si - sa ti - pha-tshi - ma - ndla taka -

Nggwane; Ngu - we we - dvwa So - ma-ndla we -

Nggwane; Ngu - we we - dvwa So - ma-ndla we -
Nggwane; Ngu - we So - ma-ndla we -

Nggwane; Ngu - we So - ma-ndla we -

-tfhu; Si - ni - ke ku - hla - ka -

-tfhu; Si - ni - ke ku - hla - ka -
-tfhu; Si - ni - ke ku - hla - ka -

-tfhu; Si - ni - ke ku - hla -

- ni - pha lo - ku - nge - na - bu - ci -

- ni - pha lo - ku - nge - na - bu - ci -
- ni - pha lo - ku - nge - na - bu - ci -

ka - ni - pha lo - ku - nge - na - bu -

* 'c' is a dental click consonant.

Free Translation

O God, bestower of the blessings of the Swazi;
We are thankful for all our good fortune,
We give praise and thanks for our King
And for our country, its hills and rivers.
Bless those in authority in Swaziland,
Thou alone art our Almighty One.
Give us wisdom without guile,
Establish us and strengthen us,
Thou Everlasting One.

Notes on Pronunciation

Vowels: There are five vowels: a, e, i, o and u. These are rendered 'pure', much as in Italian, i.e. roughly as 'ah', 'eh', 'ee', 'aw', 'oo'.

Consonants: Each consonant or consonant cluster belongs with the following vowel, not with the preceding one. Consonant clusters must be treated as single phonemes without being split up, e.g. *neh /tee /ntsah /bah* (Not *neh/teen /tsah–* or *teent /sah–*).

(1) *ng* has a 'silent g' as in Southern English 'singing' (not as in 'anger').

(2) *ngg* is as in English 'anger'.

(3) *hl* is a lateral fricative like Welsh double–L, as in 'Llanelly'.

(4) *dl* is the voiced counterpart of *hl*. (Roughly: French 'j' (as in 'measure') pronounced simultaneously with 'l'.)

(5) '*c*' is a dental click consonant– a purely suction sound produced by withdrawing the tongue-tip from the teeth (with simultaneous velar closure).
This sound is sometimes used by English speakers to express annoyance (represented by 'tch' or 'tut-tut'). In Swazi, the following vowel has a 'k–' like onset.

(6) *tsh* is like English 'ts' (not 'ch') plus slight aspiration.

(7) *k* is like English 'g'; *nk* is as in English 'anchor'; *kh* is like English 'k'.

SWEDEN

DU GAMLA, DU FRIA

Words by
RICHARD DYBECK
(1811-1877)

Folk melody
Arr. EDVIN KALLSTENIUS
(b. 1881-)

1. *Du gam - la, du fri - a, du fjäll - hö - ga Nord, du*
1. Thou an - cient, thou glo - rious, thou alp - crown - ed North, Where

tys - ta, du gläd - je - ri - ka skö - na! Jag
free - born and hap - py hearts are beat - ing! We

häl - sar dig, vä - nas - te land up - på jord, Din
hail thee, thou fair - est of lands on the earth. Thy

sol, din him - mel, di - na äng - der grö - na, din
sun, thy skies, thy flow-'ry val - leys greet - ing. Thy

sol din him - mel, di - na äng - der grö - na.
sun, thy skies, thy flow-'ry val - leys greet - ing.

2. *Du tronar på minnen från fornstora dar,*
   Då ärat ditt namn flög över jorden.
   Jag vet, att du är och du blir vad du var,
   :|: Ack, jag vill leva, jag vill dö i Norden! :|:

2. How proudly we dwell on thy great deeds of yore,
   What time thy name was famed in story;
   Thy sons still are valiant and brave as before:
   :|: In thee I'll live and die, thou land of glory! :|:

SWITZERLAND
Swiss Psalm

Schweizerpsalm
Words by L. WIDMER (1808-1868)
Cantique Suisse
CH. CHATELANET

Salmo Svizzero
Psalm Svizzer
J. A. BÜHLER

Music by
A. ZWYSSIG
(1808-1854)
Harm. G. DORET

Solenne
mf sostenuto

Ger. 1. *Trittst im Mor - gen - rot da - her,___ seh ich dich im*
Fr. 1. *Sur nos monts, quand le so - leil___ An - nonce un bril -*
It. 1. *Quan - do bion - da au - ro - ra___ Il mat - tin c'in -*
Rom.1. *In l'au - ro - ra la da - man___ at cu - gnuo - scha*
Eng.1. When the morn - ing skies grow red___ And o'er us their

mf sostenuto

Strah - len - meer,___ dich, du Hoch - er - ha - be - ner,
-lant ré - veil,___ Et pré - dit d'un plus beau jour
-do - ra___ L'al - ma mia t'a - do - ra,
bain l'u - man___ spiert e - tern do - mi - na - tur,
ra - diance shed,___ Thou, O Lord, ap - pear - eth

The music was composed by Father Alberik Zwyssig, a monk, who adapted it to Leonhard Widmer's words in 1841
This was declared the official National Anthem by the Federal Government in September 1961
for a trial period of three years, ending on 31st December 1964. This trial period has been prolonged
until further notice, pending consultations.
Reproduced by permission from *Unsere Schweizerlieder* Foetisch Frères S. A. Lausanne (All rights reserved).
Romansch words by permission from *Fluors* published by Ladinia, printed by Stamparia engladinaisa Engadin Press A.G. Samedan.

mf espressivo

Herr - li - cher!___ Wenn der Al - pen -
le - re - tour,___ Les beau - tés de
re - del - ciel,___ Quan - do l'al - pe
tuot - pus - sant! Cur ils munts stra -
In their light.___ When the Alps glow

mf espressivo

-firn___ sich___ rö - - tet,___
la___ pa - tri - - e
già___ ros - seg - - gia___
-glü - schan su - - ra,___
bright___ with___ splen - - dour,___

cresc.

Be - tet, frei - e Schwei - zer, be - tet!___
Par - lent á l'âme at - ten - dri - e;___
A pre - ga - re al - lor___ t'at - teg - gia;___
u - ra, li - ber Sviz - zer, u - ra.
Pray to God, to Him___ sur - ren - der,

cresc.

Eu - re from - me See - le ahnt,___ Eu - re from - me
Au ciel mon - tent plus joy - eux,___ Au ciel mon - tent
In fa - vor del pa - trio suol,___ In fa - vor del
Ti - a or - ma sain - ta ferm,___ Ti - a or - ma
For you feel and un - der - stand,___ For you feel and

See - le ahnt,___ Gott im heh - ren Va - ter - land,___
plus joy - eux,___ Les ac - cents d'un cœur pi - eux,___
pa - trio suol___ Cit - ta - di - no, Dio lo vuol!___
sain - ta ferm___ Dieu in tschêl, il Bap e - tern,___
un - der - stand___ That He dwell - eth in this land,___

Gott im heh - ren Va - - - ter - land!___
Les ac - cents é - mus d'un cœur pi - eux.___
Cit - ta - di - no, Dio ___ lo vuol!___
Dieu in tschêl, il' Bap ___ e - tern.___
That He dwell - - eth in ___ this land.___

GERMAN

2. *Kommst im Abendglühn daher,*
   Find ich dich im Sternenheer,
   Dich, du Menschenfreundlicher, Liebender!
   In des Himmels lichten Räumen
   Kann ich froh und selig träumen;
   Denn die fromme Seele ahnt
   Gott im hehren Vaterland.

3. *Ziehst im Nebelflor daher,*
   Such ich dich im Wolkenmeer,
   Dich, du Unergründlicher, Ewiger!
   Aus dem grauen Luftgebilde
   Bricht die Sonne klar und milde,
   Und die fromme Seele ahnt
   Gott im hehren Vaterland.

4. *Fährst im wilden Sturm daher,*
   Bist du selbst uns Hort und Wehr,
   Du, allmächtig Waltender, Rettender!
   In Gewitternacht und Grauen
   Lasst uns kindlich ihm vertrauen!
   Ja, die fromme Seele ahnt
   Gott im hehren Vaterland.

FRENCH

2. *Lorsqu'un doux rayon du soir*
   Joue encor dans le bois noir,
   Le cœur se sent plus heureux, près de Dieu.
   Loin des vains bruits de la plaine,
   L'âme en paix est plus sereine;
   Au ciel montent plus joyeux
   Les accents (émus) d'un cœur pieux.

3. *Lorsque dans la sombre nuit*
   La foudre éclate avec bruit,
   Notre cœur pressent encor le Dieu fort;
   Dans l'orage et la détresse,
   Il est notre forteresse.
   Offrons-lui des cœurs pieux
   Dieu nous bénira (du haut) des cieux.

4. *Des grands monts vient le secours,*
   Suisse, espère en Dieu toujours!
   Garde la foi des Aïeux, vis comme eux!
   Sur l'autel de la patrie
   Mets tes biens, ton cœur, ta vie!
   C'est le trésor précieux
   Que Dieu bénira (du haut) des cieux.

ITALIAN

2. *Se di nubi un velo*
   M'asconde il tuo cielo
   Pel tuo raggio anelo, Dio d'amor!
   Fuga o sole quei vapori,
   E mi rendi i tuoi favori,
   Di mia patria, deh pietà!
   Brilla, Sol di verità!

ROMANSCH

2. *Eir la saira in splendur*
   da las stailas i'l azur
   tai chattain nus creatur, tuotpussant!
   Cur cha'l firmamaint s'sclerescha
   in nos cour fidanza crescha
   Tia orma sainta ferm
   Dieu in tschêl, il Bap etern.

3. *Tü a nus nun est zoppà*
   cur il tschêl in nüvlas sta,
   Tü imperscrutabel spiert, tuotpussant!
   Tschêl e terra T'obedeschan,
   vent e nüvlas secundeschan.
   Tia orma sainta ferm
   Dieu in tschêl, il Bap etern.

4. *Eir l'orcan plü furius*
   nun At muossa main a nus
   sco il dirigent dal muond, tuotpussant!
   Eir in temporals terribels
   sun Teis uordens bain visibels.
   Tia orma sainta ferm
   Dieu in tschêl, il Bap etern.

English Translation

2. In the sunset Thou art nigh
   And beyond the starry sky,
   Thou, O loving Father, ever near.
   When to Heav'n we are departing,
   Joy and bliss Thou'lt be imparting
   For we feel and understand
   That Thou dwellest in this land.

3. When dark clouds enshroud the hills
   And grey mist the valley fills
   Yet, Thou art not hidden from Thy sons.
   Pierce the gloom in which we cower
   With Thy sunshine's cleansing power,
   Then we'll feel and understand
   That God dwelleth in this land.

4. Through the wild and stormy night,
   Thou doest shield us with Thy might,
   Omnipotent Saviour, Lord of all,
   Humbly in our God confiding,
   Conscious of His love abiding,
   Yes, we feel and understand
   That He dwelleth in our land.

AA

SWITZERLAND

Rufst du, mein Vaterland
J. R. WYSS 1811
Ci chiami, o patria
PIETRO PERI

O monts indépendants
H. RÖHRICH
Hymnus patriotic
APORTA

Composer unknown
Harm. HENRI KLING (1842-1918)

This is a popular national song, used on many occasions.
Its tune is the same as that used for Great Britain.

By permission of Foetisch Frères S.A., Lausanne, from *Unsere Schweizerlieder*

Ja - kob sah, freud - voll zum Streit! Streit!
vi - e De - tes en - fants. fants.
Ja - co - po, Non ob - li - ar! - ar!
vi - ver v'lain, Schi eir mu - rir. - rir.
built your fame, Joy - ful in strife. strife.

GERMAN

2. Da, wo der Alpenkreis
   Dich nicht zu schützen weiss,
   Wall dir von Gott.
   Stehn wir den Felsen gleich,
   Nie vor Gefahren bleich,
   Froh noch im Todesstreich,
   Schmerz uns ein Spott.

3. Frei und auf ewig frei,
   Sei unser Feldgeschrei,
   Hall unser Herz!
   Frei lebt, wer sterben kann,
   Frei, wer die Heldenbahn
   Steigt als ein Tell hinan,
   Nie hinterwärts!

FRENCH

2. Nous voulons nous unir,
   Nous voulons tous mourir
   Pour te servir.
   O notre mère!
   De nous sois fière,
   Sous ta bannière
   Tous vont partir.

3. Gardons avec fierté
   L'arbre au Grütli planté,
   La Liberté!
   Que d'âge en âge,
   Malgré l'orage,
   Cet héritage
   Soit respecté.

ITALIAN

2. La dove è debole
   Dell'Alpi l'egida
   Che il ciel tidiè
   Ti farem argine
   Coi petti intrepidi
   Anzi che cedere
   Morrem perte.

3. Ma quando arrideci
   Di pace l'iride,
   Grazie al Signor
   Ti vogliam florida,
   Diletta patria,
   Col saggio assiduo
   Nostro lavor.

ROMANSCH

2. *Scha per cas ün regent*
    Ans voless far spavent
    Oun spad e fö,
    Schi sco ün ferm torrent
    Chi sdrapa tuot davent,
    Sün l'inimi crudain
    E'l fain dar lö.

3. *Flurescha Patria,*
    In pasch e libertà
    Ed uniun!
    Sajan sincerità,
    Güsti 'ed onestà,
    Virtüd, simplicità
    Teis ornamaints.

English Translation (unofficial) by J.J.F.S.

2. Where the great Alpine shield
    Can no protection yield,
    God will sustain.
    Rocklike, we shall not fail,
    In danger never pale,
    Meet death without a wail
    And smile in pain.

3. Free and for ever free!
    This shall our watchword be,
    Our heartfelt prayer.
    Free are they who can die,
    And who with purpose high
    To every task apply
    A courage rare.

SYRIA

Words by
KHALIL MARDAM BEY

Music by
AHMAD and MUHAMMAD FLAYFEL
Arr. by HENRY COLEMAN

Allegro moderato

Hu - ma-ta al-di-ya-ri 'al - ay - kum sal-am A - bat an tu-zal-la

al-nu - fu-su al-ki - ram 'A - run u al-uru-ba - ti bay-tun ha - ram

Wa - 'ar - shu al-shu-mu - si hi - man la yu - dham Ru - bu 'u al-sha-a - mi

bur - u - ju al-'al - ai Tu - ha - ki sa - ma - a bi - 'al - i al-sa - nai

Adopted c. 1928

Ru - bu -'u al-sha-a - mi bur-u - ju al-'al - ai Tu - ha-ki sa - ma - a

bi - 'a - li al-sa - nai Fa - ar - dhun za - hat

bil - shum-usa al-wid - hai Sa - ma - un la'am - ri - ka aw kal - sa-ma.

TRANSLATION

Defenders of the realm
Peace on you;
Our proud spirits will
Not be subdued.
The abode of Arabism,
A hallowed sanctuary;
The seat of the stars,
An inviolable preserve.

Syria's plains are
Towers in the heights,
Resembling the sky
Above the clouds.
A land resplendent
With brilliant suns,
Becoming another sky
Or almost a sky.

TANZANIA
Mungu Ibariki Afrika

Words by a group of
Tanganyikans

Music by ENOCH SONTONGA*
Arr. by V. E. WEBSTER

* By permission of Lovedale Press, Cape Province, South Africa

The words of this anthem are composed from the six prize-winning entries to the competition announced by the Minister of Education on 31st July 1961. It became the National Anthem when Tanganyika achieved independence on 9th December 1961 and was retained as a National Anthem when Tanzania was formed by the union of Tanganyika and Zanzibar 26th April 1964

The music is a shorter version of N'kosi Sikelel'i Africa

Official English Translation

1. God Bless Africa.
   Bless its leaders.
   Let Wisdom Unity and
   Peace be the shield of
   Africa and its people.

   CHORUS   Bless Africa
            Bless Africa
            Bless the children of Africa.

2. God Bless Tanzania.
   Grant eternal Freedom and Unity
   to its sons and daughters.
   God Bless Tanganyika and its People.

   CHORUS   Bless Tanzania
            Bless Tanzania
            Bless the children of Tanzania.

THAILAND

Sanrasoen Phra Barami

Words by
H.R.H. Prince NARISARANUVADTIVONGS,
modified c. 1913 by
King RAMA VI (King VAJIRAVUDH)
Unofficial free translation

Music by
–. HUVITZEN

Andante maestoso

By permission of Department of Fine Arts of the Thai Government.
Adopted as National Anthem, 1934
The music was composed in 1872 for King Rama V (King Chulalongkorn)

TIBET

Words by
TRIJANG RINPOCHE

Based on a very old piece
of Tibetan sacred music

Transcribed and arranged by
W. L. REED

With dignity, but not too slow

Si - shi pen - de dö - gu jung - wi ter,

Tup - ten sam - pel nor - pu ö - nang bar. Ten - dro nor - dzin

gya - che kyong - wi gön Trin - lê kyi röl - sto gyê;

Dor - je kham - su ten - pê Cho - kün cham - tse kyong.

This anthem was composed by a group of scholars and officials
who presented it to H.H. The Dalai Lama of Tibet in 1960.
The words are by the Dalai Lama's tutor, Trigang Rinpoche.
It is not used inside Tibet at the present time.

shi - di — pe - la jor. Pö - jong ten - drö ge - tzen nyi - ö
kyi, Tra - shi ö - nang bum - du — tro - wi
zi, Na - cho mün - pi yu - le gye - gyur chi.

The source of temporal and spiritual wealth of joy and boundless benefits,
The Wish-fulfilling Jewel of the Buddha's Teaching, blazes forth radiant light,
The All-protecting Patron of the Doctrine and of all sentient beings
By his actions stretches forth his influence like an ocean;
By his eternal Vajra-nature
His compassion and loving care extend to beings everywhere.
May the celestially appointed Government of Gawa Gyaden achieve the heights of glory,
And increase its fourfold influence and prosperity.
May a golden age of joy and happiness spread once more through the three regions of Tibet,
And may its temporal and spiritual splendour shine again.
May the Buddha's Teaching spread in all the ten directions and lead all beings in the universe to glorious peace.
May the spiritual Sun of the Tibetan Faith and People,
Emitting countless rays of auspicious light,
Victoriously dispel the strife of darkness.

TOGO

Words by ALEX CASIMIR-DOSSEH
Trans. from French to Ewe by the
REV. FATHER H. KWAKUME

Music by
ALEX CASIMIR-DOSSEH
Arr. by HENRY COLEMAN

Ewe 1. Mie-do gbe na wo, to-gui-wo!___ nyi-gba! Woe de lo-lo wo-
French 1. Sa-lut à Toi, pa-ys de nos___ a-ïeux! Toi qui les ren-dais

-me, nu-sè kple tu-fa-fa. Wu-do-do kple Ka-lè-wo-wo-
forts, pai-si-bles et joy-eux Cul-ti-vant ver-tu, vail-lan-ce

___ fe do-me ye mie nyi. Le dzi-du-du nu-ta-sè-toe me la, A-
___ Pour la pos-té-r-ité. Que vien-nent les ty-rans, ton cœur sou-pi-re

This National Anthem was chosen as a result of a competition
between Togolese composers. It was first played on 27th April,
1960, the date on which Togo attained independence.

EWE

2. *Miawo do ne le dekawowo me.*
   Esia enye miafe dzime dzodzro vevieto
   Naneke magbahe mo na miafe nyatiatiaa o.
   Miawo'si me ko ye wo dzogbenyui kple wo ngoyiyi le.
   Yata miade kluvi-kokutiawo da
   Anukwaredidi nano mia me daa!
   Mina miasubo Denyigba la!
   Togonyigba la nezu nami
   Abe hehea fe Sikakpe ene.

FRENCH

2. *Dans l'unité nous voulons te servir*
   C'est bien lá de nos coeurs le plus ardent désir
   Clamons fort notre devise
   Que rien ne peut ternir.
   Seuls artisans de ton bonheur ainsi que de ton avenir,
   Brisons partout les chaînes, la traîtrise
   Et nons te jurons toujours fidélité
   Et aimer, servir, se dépasser,
   Faire encore de toi sans nous lasser
   Togo Chéri, l'Or de l'Humanité.

English Translation

1. Hail to thee, land of our forefathers,
   Thou who made them strong, peaceful and happy,
   Men who for posterity cultivated virtue and bravery.
   Even if tyrants shall come, thy heart yearns towards freedom.
   Togo arise! Let us struggle without faltering.
   Victory or death, but with dignity.
   God almighty, Thou alone hast made Togo prosper.
   People of Togo arise! Let us build the nation.

2. To serve thee in unity is the most burning desire of our hearts.
   Let us shout aloud our motto
   That nothing can tarnish.
   We the only builders of thy happiness and of thy future,
   Everywhere let us break chains and treachery,
   And we swear to thee for ever faith, love, service, untiring zeal,
   To make thee yet, beloved Togo, a golden example for humanity.

TONGA

Harmonised by
HENRY COLEMAN

Moderato

'E   'O - tu - a   Ma - fi - ma -   fi,
Oh   Al - migh - ty   God   a - bove,   Thou

Ko   ho   mau 'Ei - mi   ko - e,   Ko   Koe ko   e
art   our   Lord   and   sure   de - fence,   In   our good - ness

fa - la - la 'anga, Mo   e 'of - a   ki Tong - a:
we   do   trust Thee   And   our Ton - ga   Thou dost love;

'A - fio hi - fo 'e- mau lo - tu
Hear our prayer, for though un - seen We

'Ai - a 'ok - u mau fai ni, Mo ke ta - li
know that Thou hast blessed our land; Grant our earn - est

ho mau lo - to 'O ma - lu - 'i 'a Tu - pou.
sup - pi - ca - tion, Guard and save Tu - pou our Queen.

TRINIDAD AND TOBAGO

Words and Music by
PATRICK S. CASTAGNE (b. 1916)

Alla marcia moderato

Forged from the love of li - ber-ty, in the fires of hope and prayer, With bound-less faith in our des - ti - ny, we so-lemn-ly de - clare:

The National Anthem officially came into use at midnight on
31st August 1962 at the Flag Raising Ceremony held outside
Parliament Buildings at Port of Spain, Trinidad.   It was
chosen as the result of a competition held by the Government.
Patrick Castagne is well known in the West Indies as composer, producer and broadcaster.
Published by permission of the Trinidad and Tobago High Commission, London.

Side by side we stand, Is-lands of the blue Car-ib-bean Sea.

This our na-tive land, we pledge our lives to thee. Here ev'ry

creed and race find an e-qual place, And may God bless our na-tion. Here ev'ry

creed and race find an e-qual place, And may God bless our na-tion.

TUNISIA

Words by
JALLAL EDDINE ENNAKACHE
English translation by
Dr. ISMAIL HASSAN
Versification by
T. M. CARTLEDGE

Music by
SALAH EL MAHDI
(Piano transcription by
T. M. CARTLEDGE)

Ä - LÄ KhÄL-LI-DÎ YÄ DI - MÄ-NÄL-GhÄ-WÂ-LÎ DƷI-
Im - mor - tal and pre - cious the blood we have shed for our

-HÂ - DÄL - WA - TAN LI - TAḤ - RÎ - RI KhAD - RA - 'I -
dear fath - er - land. In or - der to free our green

-NÄ LÄ - NU BÄ - LÎ BI AK - SAL MI - ḤAN DƷI -
land a - ny hard - ship we glad - ly will stand. The

Officially adopted 20th March 1958

HÄ-DUN TA-ḤAL-LÄ BI NAS-RIM-MU-BÎN 'AL-ÄL GhA-SI-BÎN 'AL-
fight is made sweet by a vic-to-ry sure Re-mov-ing the yoke we've

-ÄL HA-KI-MIN TU-GhÂT IZ-ZÄ-MÄN NÄ-
had to en-dure. The fire we con-front as

-KhU-DUL-LÄ HÎB BI RU-HIL HA-BIB ZA-'IM IL-WA-TAN
faith-ful we keep The spi-rit of our great lead-er Ha-bib.

Fine

2. WÄRIThNÄL-ɟILÂDÄ WÄ MÄɟDÄN-NIDÂL
WÄ FÎ ARDINÂ MASRA'UL-GhÂSIBÎN.
WÄ SÂLÄT ASÂTÎLINÂ FIN-NIZÂL
TÄMÛɟU BI 'ABTÂLINÄL-FÂTIHÎN.
LIWÂ 'UL-KIFÂHI BIHÂThÄSh-ShIMÂL
RÄFÄ-'NÂHU YÄWMÄL-FIDÂ BIL-YÄMÎN.

3. ShÄBÂBÄL-'OLÂ 'IZZUNÂ BIL-HIMÂ
WÄ 'IZZUL-HIMÂ BISh-ShÄBÂBIL-'ÄTÎD.
LINÂ HIMMÄTUN TÂLÄTIL-'ÄNɟUMÂ
TU 'ÎDUL-MÄ 'ÂLÎ WÄ TÄBNIL-ɟÄDÎD.
FÄHÄYYUL-LIWÂ KhÂFIQÄN FIS-SÄMÂ
BI 'IZZIN WÄ FÄKhRIN WÄ NASRIN MÄɟÎD.

2. The glory and fight we inherit today.
Oppressors were fought here on this battleground.
Our legions in fury attacked in the field
As heroes in waves let their war-cries resound.
The banner of war in the North we have raised,
By oath we to ransom our land all are bound.

3. O noble the youth, our defence you assure,
Defending our honour, as ready you be.
Our strong aspirations reach up to the sky
That greatness return and a new day we see.
The flag, as it waves in the sky, now salute
With honour and glory and great victory.

Key to phonetic transliteration of Arabic text

^ for long vowels
Û as *oo* in *pool*
U nearer *u* in *put*
Ä as *a* in *cat*
A as *a* in *rather*
W at end of syllable as *oo*
Th① as *th* in *thing*

Th② as *th* in *this*
H aspirated at back of mouth
Kh like hard *ch* in German *Buch*
Gh like gutteral *r* in French *rang*
'like last *a* in *China*
Q like *k* sound at back of mouth

TURKEY
Istıklâl Marsi
THE MARCH OF INDEPENDENCE

Words by
MEHMET AKIF ERSOY
English versification by
T. M. CARTLEDGE

Music by
ZEKI ÜNGÖR
Arr. by
T. M. CARTLEDGE

1. Kork - ma sön - mez bu sa - fak - lar - da yü - zen - al san - cak Sön - me - den yur - du - mun üs - tün - de tü - ten en son o - cak. O

1. Fear not and be not dis - mayed, This crim - son flag will nev - er fade. It is the last hearth that's burn - ing for my na - tion and we know for

* lower notes optional for bass or alto voices.

Pronunciation: ş like sh
c like j
ö and ü as in German.
ı (i without dot) more like final a of china

Officially adapted as Turkey's National Anthem 12th March 1921

be - nim mil - le - ti - min._____ Yıl - dı - zı -
sure that it will nev - er fail._____ It is my

- dır par - la - ya-cak. O be - nim - dir,_____ o be - nim
na - tion's star that ev - er forth will shine,_____ It is my

mil - le - ti - min-dir an - cak._____ 2. Çat -
na - tion's star and it is mine._____ 2.Frown - lâl._____

2. *Çatma kurban olayım çehreni ey nazlı hilâl*
Kahraman ırkıma bir gül ne bu şiddet bu celâl
Sana olmaz dökülen kanlarımız sonra helâl
Hakkıdır hakka tapan milletimin istiklâl.

2. Frown not, fair crescent, for I
Am ready e'en to die for thee.
Smile now upon my heroic nation, leave this anger,
   lest the blood shed for thee umblessed be.
Freedom's the right of this my nation,
Yes, freedom for us who worship God and seek what's right.

UGANDA

Words by
GEORGE W. KAKOMA and **PETER WYNGARD**

Music by
GEORGE W. KAKOMA

1. Oh U - gan - da! may God up - hold thee, We

lay our fu - ture in thy hand. U - ni - ted, free, For

lib - er - ty To - geth - er we'll al - ways stand.

2. Oh Uganda! the land of freedom.
Our love and labour we give,
And with neighbours all
At our country's call
In peace and friendship we'll live.

3. Oh Uganda! the land that feeds us
By sun and fertile soil grown.
For our own dear land,
We'll always stand:
The Pearl of Africa's Crown.

This National Anthem was selected through a competition, and came
into use when Uganda became independent on 9th October, 1962.
G.W. Kakoma is a Music Master employed in the Education Department,
and P. Wyngard an English Master at Makerere University College.

UKRAINE

Words by
PAUL CHUBYNSKYI (1839-1884)

Music by
MICHAEL VERBYTSKYI (1815-1870)
Arr. by HENRY COLEMAN

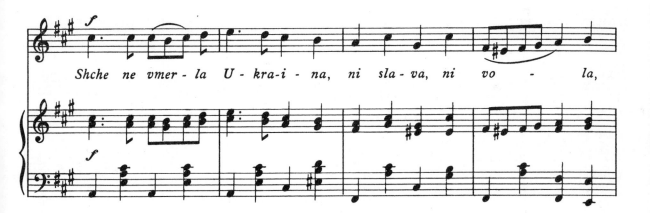

Shche ne vmer - la U - kra-i - na, ni sla - va, ni vo - la,

Shche nam brat - tia mo - lo-di - i u - smikh-net'-sia do - la:

Performed as a choral work in 1864 in the Ukrainian Theatre in Lviv,
it became officially recognised as the National Anthem in 1917, but is
not at present used in that country where the U.S.S.R. anthem is officially
used.

Zkhy - nut' na - shi vo - ro-zhen'-ky, yak ro-ssa na son - ci,

Za - pa-nu - yem i my, brat-tia, u svo-ii sto-ron - ci,

Du - shu, ti - lo my po-lo - zhym za na-shu svo-bo - - du

I po-ka-zhem, shcho my, brat - tia, ko-zać-ko-ho ro - du.

Du - shu ti - lo my po - lo - zhym za na - shu svo - bo - du

I po-ka zhem, shcho my, brat - tia, ko - zać - ko - ho ro - du.

English Translation

Ukraine has not died yet,
As freedom cannot die,
Be hopeful valiant brothers,
Our glory will revive.

Who us enslave, will perish,
As dew within sun's ray,
The enlightened rule of kin
Our country will regain.

Our soul and body willing
To give for liberty,
O, brothers, we are nearing
The path to victory.

UNION OF SOVIET SOCIALIST REPUBLICS

Words by
S. MIKHALKOV and EL-REGISTAN
Translated by
HERBERT MARSHALL

Music by
A.V. ALEXANDROV (d. 1946)

1. *So - yuz ne - ru-shi - mi res - pub - lik svo-bod - nikh Splo - ti - la na-ve-ki Ve - li - ka - ya Rus'. Da zdrast - vu - yet soz - dan-ni vo - lei na - ro - dov, Ye - di - ni mo-gu - chi So - vyet - ski So-yuz!*

1. Un - break - a - ble U - nion of free - born Re-pub - lics, Great Rus - sia has weld - ed for - ev - er to stand; Cre - a - ted in strug - gle by will of the peo - ples, U - ni - ted and might - y, our So - vi - et Land!

Pronunciation: "Kh" = "Ch" in Scottish "loch",
"Zh" = "S" in English "measure",
' = palatalisation of preceeding consonant

This became officially the Soviet National Anthem
in 1943, replacing the "International."

CHORUS

Sláv - sya,_ O - tye - chest-vo na - she svo -
Sing to_ our_ Mo - ther-land, glo - ry_ un -

-bod - no-ye, Druzh - bi na - ro - dov na-dyozh - ni op - lot!_
-dy - ing, Bul - wark of peo - ples in bro - ther-hood strong!_

Zna - mya_ so - vyet - sko-ye, zna - mya_ na -
Flag of_ the_ So - vi - ets, peo - ples'_ flag_

-rod - no-ye Pust' ot po - be - di kpo - be - dye vye-dyot! 2. Skvoz'
fly - ing, Lead us from vic - t'ry to vic - to - ry on! 2. Through

cc

Pust' ot po-be-di kpo-be-dye vye-dyot!
Lead us from vic-t'ry to vic-to-ry on!

2. *Skvoz' grozi siyalo nam solntse svobodi,*
   I Lenin veliki nam put' ozaril.
   Nas virastil Stalin na vernost' narodu,
   Na trud i na podvigi nas vdokhnovil.

3. *Mi armiyu nashu rastili vsrazhenyakh,*
   Zakhvatchikov podlikh sdorogi smetyom!
   Mi vbitvakh reshayem sud'bupokoleni,
   Mi kslavye Otchiznu svoyu povyedyom!

---

2. Through tempests the sunrays of freedom have cheered us,
   Along the new path where great Lenin did lead.
   Be true to the people, thus Stalin has reared us,
   Inspired us to labour and valorous deed!

3. Our army grew up in the heat of grim battle,
   Barbarian invaders we'll swiftly strike down.
   In combat the fate of the future we settle,
   Our country we'll lead to eternal renown.

UNITED ARAB REPUBLIC

Words by
SALAH SHAHYN

Music by
KAMAL ATTAWYL

Allegro moderato

Wal - la Za-man Ya Si - la - hi   Ish - taq-ti Lak Fi Ki- -fa - hi   In - taq We Qul A - na Sa - hi   Ya Har - b Wal - la Za - man.

Interlude

This was a song which achieved great national popularity in 1956.
The National Anthem was derived from it, and first used on 20th May, 1960.
The chorus only is sung, followed by an instrumental interlude, then a repeat of the chorus.

Wal - la Za-man Ya Si - la - hi

Ish - taq-ti Lak Fi Ki-fa - hi In - taq We Qul A - na

Sa - hi Ya Har-b Wal - la Za-man.

Transliteration

1. *Walla Zaman 'Algunud*
   Zahfa Bitir'id Ri'ud
   Halfa Tiruh Lam Ti'ud
   Illa Binasr Al-zaman.

2. *Hummu Wu Dummu Al-sufuf*
   Shilu Al-hayat 'Alkufuf
   Yama Al-'adu Rah Yishuf
   Minkum Binar El-fida.

3. *Ya Magd Ya Magdina*
   Yalli Itbanait 'Andana
   Bishaqana Wa Kaddina
   'Umrak Ma Tibqa Hawan.

4. *Masr Al-hurra Min Yihmiha*
   Nihmiha Bislahna
   Ardh Al-thawra Min Yifdiha
   Nifdiha Biarwahna.

5. *Al-shab Biyizhaf Zayy El-nur*
   Al sha'b Gebal Al-sha'b Bhur
   Burkan Ghadban Burkan Biyfur
   Zilzal Biyshuqq Lohom Fi Qbur.

Free Translation

Chorus   O! my weapon!
How I long to clutch thee!
Respond, awake and alert,
For valiant combat.

1. Hail, gallant troops,
   Dashing with thunderous roar,
   Swearing never to return
   Except with epoch-making victory.

2. Rise and raise a host,
   With loyal hearts ready for sacrifice.
   Oh! the horror the enemy shall suffer
   Through the fire of your zeal.

3. O! glory of our Country,
   Achieved with our own efforts alone,
   By hard hours of toil,
   Never to be wasted or endangered.

4. Who shall protect Free Egypt?
   We shall protect it with our lives.
   Land of the Revolution, who will sacrifice
   We will, with our lives.   for her sake?

5. The people advance like the light,
   The people stand like mountains and seas,
   Angry volcanos, erupting volcanos,
   Earthquakes digging graves for the enemy.

UNITED STATES OF AMERICA
The Star-Spangled Banner

Words by
FRANCIS SCOTT KEY (1779-1843)

Music by
J. STAFFORD SMITH
(1750-1836)

rock - ets' red glare, the bombs burst - ing in

air, Gave proof thro' the night that our

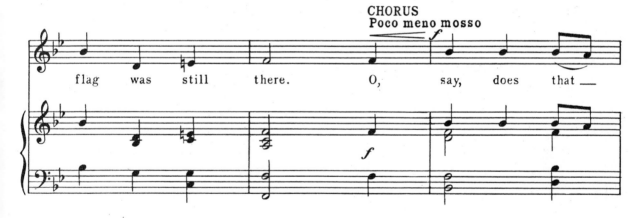

CHORUS
Poco meno mosso

flag was still there. O, say, does that ___

Star - Span - gled Ban - ner ___ yet ___ wave ___ O'er the

land _____ of the free and the home of the brave?

2. On the shore, dimly seen thro' the mists of the deep,
   Where the foe's haughty host in dread silence reposes,
   What is that which the breeze, o'er the towering steep,
   As it fitfully blows, half conceals, half discloses?
   Now it catches the gleam of the morning's first beam,
   In full glory reflected now shines on the stream;
   'Tis the Star-Spangled Banner, O long may it wave
   O'er the land of the free and the home of the brave.

3. O thus be it ever when free man shall stand
   Between their loved homes and the war's desolation!
   Blest with vict'ry and peace, may the heav'n-rescued land
   Praise the Pow'r that hath made and preserved us a nation.
   Then conquer we must, for our cause it is just,
   And this be our motto: "In God is our trust."
   And the Star-Spangled Banner in triumph shall wave
   O'er the land of the free and the home of the brave.

UPPER VOLTA

Words and Music by
Abbé ROBERT OUÉDRAOGO
Arr. by HENRY COLEMAN

1 Fiè - re Vol - ta de mes A - ïeux, Ton so - leil ar-dent et glo-ri-eux

Te re-vêt d'or et de clar-té, O, Rei-ne dra-pée de lo-yau - té.

CHORUS
Nous te fe - rons et plus forte et plus bel - le,

Approved as the National Anthem by the Upper Volta National Assembly on 3rd August 1960

A ton a-mour, nous res-te-rons fi-dè-les, Et nos cœurs, vi-

-brants de fier-té, Ac-cla-me-ront ta beau-té. -té.

2. Vers l'horizon lève les yeux,
   Frémis aux accents tumultueux
   De tes fiers enfants tous dressés,
   Promesse d'avenirs caressés.

3. Le travail de ton sol brûlant
   Sans fin trempera les cœurs ardents,
   Et les vertus de tes enfants
   Le ceindront d'un diadème triomphant.

4. Que Dieu te garde en sa bonté,
   Que du bonheur de ton sol aimé,
   L'Amour des frères soit la clé,
   Honneur, Unité et Liberté.

Free Translation by ELIZABETH P. COLEMAN

CHORUS We will make thee stronger and more beautiful,
We will stay faithful to thy love,
And our hearts, beating with pride,
Will acclaim thy beauty.

1. Proud Volta of my forefathers,
   Thy glorious burning sun
   Clothes thee in golden light,
   O Queen draped in loyalty.

2. Raise thine eyes towards the future
   Vibrating with tumultuous voices
   Of thy proud children, standing ready,
   The promise of a happy future.

3. The toil on thy burning soil
   Will never cease to brace the fervent hearts
   And the virtues of thy children
   Will circle it with a triumphal crown.

4. May God protect thee in His goodness;
   For the happiness of thy beloved land,
   May brotherly love be the key
   And honour, unity and liberty.

URUGUAY

Words by
FRANCISCO ACUÑA de FIGUEROA (1790-1862)
English versification by
T. M. CARTLEDGE

Music by
FERNANDO QUIJANO and FRANCISCO J. DEBALLI
Arr. by G. GRASSO

¡O-rien-ta-les, la Patria o la tum-ba! ¡Li-ber-tad, o con glo-ria mo-rir! ¡O-rien-ta-les la Patria o la tum-ba! ¡Li-ber-

East-ern lands-men, our coun-try or the tomb now! Li-ber-ty or with glo-ry to die! East-ern lands-men, our coun-try or the tomb now! Li-ber-

Reproduced by permission of
Recordi Americana S.A.E.C. Buenos Aires
Officially adopted as the National Anthem by a government decree of 27th July 1848
The author was a poet and head of the National Library of Uruguay.

-tad o con glo-ria mo-rir! Es el vo-to que el al-ma pro-
-ty or with glo-ry to die! This the vow that our souls all have

-nun - cia y que he - ro - i-cos sa-bre-mos cum-plir, es el
tak - en And know how__ to ful-fil,— cour-age high, This the

vo - to que el al - ma pro - nun - cia y que he-
vow that our souls all have tak - en And know

-roi - cos sa-bre - mos cum - plir, que sa -
how to ful-fil, cour-age high, to ful -

bre - - mos cum - plir, es el
-fil, cour - age high, This the

cresc. molto

vo - to que el al - ma pro - nun - cia y que he -
vow that our souls all have tak - en And know

-roi - cos sa - bre - mos cum - plir, que sa -
how to ful - fil, cour - age high, to ful -

- bre - - mos cum - plir,
-fil, cour - age high.

sa - bre - mos cum - plir,   sa - bre - mos cum -
ful - fil, cour - age high,   ful - fil, cour - age

- plir, sa - bre - mos cum - plir.
high, ful - fil, cour - age high.

Fine

Moderato

p VERSE

¡Li - ber - tad,! ¡li - ber - tad,! O - rien - ta - les Es - te
Li - ber - ty, Li - ber - ty, East - ern lands - men! 'Twas this

grí - to a la Pa - tria sal - vó! Que a sus bra - vos en fie - ras ba -
cry saved our coun - try of yore, And in - flam - ing its he - roes with

-ta - llas, De en - tu - sias - mo su - bli - me in - fla - mó. ¡Li - ber-
pas - sion, Pre - pared them for fierce bat - tles' roar. Li - ber-

-mó. De es - te don sa - cro - san - to la glo - ria me - re-
roar. The___ glo - ry from this gift so sac - red We all

-ci - mos; Ti - ra - nos tem - blad! ¡Ti - ra - nos tem-
mer - it, A - way___ ty - ran - ny! A - way ty - ran-

f CHORUS

-blad! Ti - ra - nos tem - blad! Ah! ¡Li - ber-
-ny! A - way, ty - ran - ny! Ah! Li - ber-

VERSE

-tad___ en la lid___ cla - ma - re - - mos y mu-
-ty___ in the fight___ we shall cry___ for, And ex-

-rien - do tam - bién___ li - ber - tad!   ¡Li-ber-
-pir - ing still cry for li - ber - ty!   Li-ber-

f CHORUS

Allegro

-tad___ en la lid___ cla - ma - re - mos y mu-
-ty___ in the fight___ we shall cry___ for And ex-

-rien - do tam - bién   li - ber - tad!___ y mu-
-pir - ing still cry   Li - ber - ty!___ And ex-

-rien - do tam-bien li - ber - tad!
-pir - ing, still cry Li - ber - ty!

ff

tam - bién li - ber - tad!
still cry Li - ber - ty!

tam - bién li - ber - tad!
still cry Li - ber - ty!

dal % al Fine

f

O - rien -
East - ern

f

dal % al Fine

VATICAN
Marcia Pontificale

No words

Music by
CHARLES GOUNOD (1818-1893)

This became the official hymn in 1949. It is played (1) In the presence of the Holy Father. (2) In the presence of one of his Special Legates. (3) On the occasion of the presentation of Credential Letters by a Nuncio of the Holy See.

The music is reproduced by permission of Institut fur Auslandsbezihungen, Stuttgart, and taken from *Die National-Hymnen Der Erde*.

VENEZUELA

Words by
VICENTE SALIAS
English versification
by **T. M. CARTLEDGE**

Music by
JUAN JOSÉ LANDAETA (c. 1810)
Arr. by **HENRY COLEMAN**

The author and composer, natives of Venezuela, were both shot in
1814 during the struggle for the liberty of their country.
Adopted as National Anthem, 25th May 1881, by a government decree

el vil e - go - is - mo que otra vez triun - fó.
The foul self - ish ty - rant Who once tri - umphed here.

2 *Gritemos con brío:*
   Muera la opresión!
   Compatriotas fieles
   la fuerza es la unión:
   y desde el Empireo
   el Supremo Autor
   un sublime aliento
   al pueblo infundió.
   CORO

3 *Unida con lazos*
   que el cielo formó,
   la América toda
   existe en Nación;
   y si el despotismo
   levanta la voz
   seguid el ejemplo
   que Caracas dió.
   CORO

2 Let's cry out aloud:
   May oppression banished be!
   Faithful countrymen, your strength
   Lives in your unity.
   And from highest heaven
   The great Creater breathed;
   A spirit sublime
   Among us here bequeathed.
   CHORUS

3 United by bonds
   Made by heav'n's creative hand,
   All America exists
   As one united land.
   And if tyranny
   Should dare to raise its head,
   Let all of us follow
   Where Caracas has led.
   CHORUS

VIET-NAM

Quôc Thiêù Viêt-Nam

Words and Music by
LUU HUU PHUOC, 1943

Tempo di Marcia

Này Thanh-niên đi đứng lên đáp lời sông núi____ Đồng lòng cùng

đi đi đi mở đường khai lối.____ Vì non sông nườc xửa, truyền

muôn năm chớ quên. Nào anh em Băć-Nam cùng nhau ta kết đoàn. Hồn

Adopted as National Anthem in 1945

thanh xuân như gương trong sáng.____ Dừng tiếc máu nóng tài xin

cresc.

ráng.____ Thời khó thế khó khó làm yêu ta, Dẫu muôn chông gai vững

lòng chi sá Đường mỗi kiếp phóng mắt nhìn xa bốn phường Tung

cánh hồn thiếu niên ai đó can - trường. Thanh-niên ơi!____ ta quyết đi

đến cùng. Thanh-niên ơi! ____ ta nguyền đem hết lòng Tiến lên! dòng tiên ve

vang đời sống. Chờ quên rằng ta là giống Lạc - Hồng. ____

Free Translation

Youth of Viet-nam, arise! And at our Country's call
Single in heart let us open the way; let us keep in mind
Our millenary history. From North to South, brothers,
Let us unite. Our young hearts are crystal pure;
Unsparing of our ardent blood, let our efforts increase.
No danger, no obstacle can hold us back.
Despite a thousand trials our courage is unshaken.
On this new road our eyes embrace the horizon,
Our soaring youthful spirit is undauntable.
Youth of Viet-nam, to the very end! this we resolve.
To give ourselves completely, this we vow.
Forward together for a glorious life,
Remember we are the sons of the Lac-Hong.

WALES
Hen Wlad fy Nhadau
LAND OF MY FATHERS

Welsh words by
EVAN JAMES
(1809-1893)
English Translation by
W. S. GWYNN WILLIAMS

Melody by
JAMES JAMES (1856)
Arr. by **W. S. GWYNN WILLIAMS**

Moderato

Mae hen wlad fy nhad-au yn
The land of my fath-ers is

an nwyl i___ mi, Gwlad beirdd a chan-tor-ion, en-wog-ion o
dear un-to___ me, Old land where the min-strels are hon-oured and

fri; Ei gwr-ol ry-fel-wyr,gwlad-gar-wyr tra___ mâd, Tros
free; Its war-ring de-fen-ders so gal-lant and___ brave, For

CHORUS

rydd-id coll-as-ant eu gwaed._____ Gwlad, gwlad,
free-dom their life's blood they gave._____ Home, home,

This national song was first sung at the famous Llangollen Eisteddfod
of 1858, and is now regarded as having the status of a National Anthem.
It is also sung as a National Anthem in Brittany, to a Breton translation by Taldir.

pleid - iol wyf___ i'm gwlad, Tra môr yn___ fur i'r
true___ am I___ to home, While seas se - cure the

bur hoff bau, O bydd - ed i'r hen-iaith bar - hau.
land so___ pure, O may the old lan-guage en - dure.

2. Hen Gymru fynyddig, paradwys y bardd,
Pob dyffryn, pob clogwyn i'm golwg sydd hardd;
Trwy deimlad gwladgarol, mor swynol yw si
Ei nentydd, afonydd, i mi.

    Gwlad, gwlad, etc.

3. Os treisiodd y gelyn fy ngwlad tan ei droed,
Mae hen iaith y Cymry mor fyw ag erioed;
Ni luddiwyd yr awen gan erchyll law brad,
Na thelyn berseiniol fy ngwlad.

    Gwlad, gwlad, etc.

2. Old land of the mountains, the Eden of bards,
Each gorge and each valley a loveliness guards;
Through love of my country, charmed voices will be
Its streams, and its rivers, to me.

    Home, home, etc.

3. Though foemen have trampled my land 'neath their feet,
The language of Cambria still knows no retreat;
The muse is not vanquished by traitor's fell hand,
Nor silenced the harp of my land.

    Home, home, etc.

WESTERN SAMOA
The Banner of Freedom

Words and Music by
SAUNI I. KURESA (b.1904)
Arr. by HENRY COLEMAN

Moderato

Sa-moa, tu-la'i ma si-si ia lau fu'a, lou pa-le le - a; Sa-moa, tu-la'i ma si - si ia lau fu'a, lou pa-le-le - a; Va-Pu-

Lyrics under the staves:

-ai i na fe- tū o loo ua a-gia-gi-a ai; Le
le____ ma Tu- mu- a, I- tu 'au ma A- la- taua, A-

fa- ai- lo- ga lea o Ie- su na ma- liu ai mo Sa-
-i- ga i le Tai ma le Vaa o Fono- ti, Mā-lō Tau-

-moa Oi! Sa- moa e, u- u ma- u lau
-tai! Oi! Ma- lie toa ma Tu- pu- a, Le

pu- le ia fa- a- va- va - u.] 'Au- a e te
Ma- lo₀ ia fa- a- va- va - u. }

fe - fe, o le Atua lo ta fa'a vae — O lo - ta

Sa'o lo - to - ga, Sa - moa, tu - la'i, ia

a - gia - gia lau Fu'a lou pa - le le - a.

Samoa, arise and raise your banner that is your crown.

Oh! see and behold the stars on the waving banner
They are a sign that Samoa is able to lead.

Oh! Samoa hold fast
Your freedom for ever.

Do not be afraid; as you are founded on God;
Our treasured precious liberty.
Samoa, arise and wave
Your banner that is your crown.

YEMEN

Arr. by HENRY COLEMAN

Sa-lim - ta I-ma - man Li 'ar - shil - bi la - di

wa-raf-ra-fa haw-la 'u - la - kal 'a - lam

Wa za-la bi-'az — mi-ka daw-rul fa-sa — di

Wa-qad-da-sa-kas sai — fu ba' — dal qa-lam

fa-dum liz-za-'a-ma-ti in — dal ji-had

Wa 'in-das sa-la-mi wa 'in dal ka-ram

wa'Ish lil ka-ra - ma - ti fi kul - li nad

ma-li - kan li 'ar - shil hu - da Wal hi - mam.

Free Translation

May you be safe as to the country's throne Imam,
And may the herald round your glory flutter,
For by your will corruption's reign dissolved,
And next to pen the sword to you did bow.
May you live long to be in strife the head,
In peace to be abreast, and of philanthropy the King.
May you live long for dignity in every sphere,
And of the throne of piety and zeal the monarch.

YUGOSLAVIA

Words by
(1) JOVAN DJORDJEVIC (1826-1900)
(2) ANTUN MIHANOVIĆ (1796-1861)
(3) SIMÓN JENKO (1835-1869)
English words by LORRAINE NOEL FINLAY★

Music by
(1) DAVORIN JENKO (1835-1914)
(2) LICHTENEGGER (c.1850)
(3) DAVORIN JENKO (1835-1914)
Arr. by HENRY COLEMAN

Bo - že - prav - de,_ ti što spa - se, Od pro - pa - sti
God of jus - tice,_ save thy_ peo - ple, Lord, pro - tect us

do sad - nas, Čuj i od sad - na - še_ gla - se
day by_ day; Hear our_ voi - ces_ sup - pli - cat - ing,

I od - sad nam bu - di - spas! Le - pa na - ša
Grant sal - va - tion now, we_ pray. Bless - ed home - land,

This National Anthem is a combination, made in 1918, of the National Anthems
of the Serbs, Croats and Slovenes.   Part 1 is taken from the Serbian Anthem,
Part 2 from the Croatian, Part 3 from the Slovene, and the last 4 bars from the
Serbian.
The National Anthem "Hej Slaveni" is now officially used in Yugoslavia.

★By permission of the Boston Music Company, Boston, Massachusetts (Chappell & Co. Ltd. London).

do-mo-vi-no, Oj___ ju-nač-ka, zem-ljo mi-la.
we sa-lute thee, Fair-est proud soil, he-roes hold__ dear.

Sta-re sla-ve de-do-vi-no, da___ bi vaz-da čast-na bi-la. Na-
Fa-ther-land, al-legiance we pledge, Hon-our-ing__ thee, land without peer. "Ad-

Tempo marziale

-prej za-sta-va sla-ve, na boj ju-nač-ka kri. Za
-vance with ban-ners wav-ing! Fight on!" our he-roes cry. To

bla-gar o-čet nja-ve naj pu-ška go-vo-ri! Na-
save our coun-try's glo-ry The roar-ing guns re-ply. "Ad-

-prej za-sta-va, sla - ve, na boj, ju-nač-ka kri! Za

-vance with ban - ners wav - ing! Fight on!" our he-roes cry. To

bla - gar o - čet nja - ve naj pu-ška go-vo-ri!

save our coun-try's glo - ry The roar-ing guns re - ply.

Bo - že, spa-si, Bo-že, hra - ni, na - šeg Kra-lja. i - naš rod!

God pro-tect our no-ble mon - arch, God watch o - ver great and small,

Kra - lja Pe-tra, Bo - že, hra - ni, mo - li ti - se - sav naš rod!

God sus-tain and guide King Pe - ter, God de-fend and keep us all.

YUGOSLAVIA
Hej Slaveni

Words Anon.

Traditional
Arr. by HENRY COLEMAN

Maestoso

Hej Sla-ve - ni, jo-šte ži - vi___ duh na-ših dje-
Fel - low Slavs, the spi-rit of___ your___ an-cient breed still

- do - va, dok za na - rod sr-ce bi - je___
tri - umphs, while your youth still knows the cause___ of the

nij-ho-vih si - no - va. Ži - vi, ži - vi, duh sla-ven - ski
wor-ker and the pea - sant. Long to live Slav - on - ic spi - rit

Originally composed about the middle of the 19th century as
an anthem of the Slavonic movement for the Union of Slavs
and afterwards adopted by some of the Slavonic countries as
their National Anthem. It became the National Anthem of
Yugoslavia in 1945.

3 Let the tempest rage about us,
  Sweeping all before it —
  Rock is riven, oak uplifted,
  Aye, the whole earth trembles, —

4 But we stand steadfast and constant
  Like a granite mountain.
  Curses be on all betrayers
  False to our glad homeland!

ZAMBIA

Music by ENOCH SONTONGA★
Arr. by Mrs. Walters and D. W. Dunn

1. Stand and sing of Zam-bia, proud and free, Land of work and joy in u-ni-ty, Vic-tors in the strug-gle for the right, We've won We have won free-dom's fight. All one, strong and free.
2. A-fri-ca is our own mo-ther-land, Fash-ion'd with and blessed by God's good hand, Let us all her peo-ple join as one, Bro-thers un-der the sun. All one, strong and free.
3. One land and one na-tion is our cry, Dig-ni-ty and peace 'neath Zam-bia's sky, Like our no-ble ea-gle in its flight, Zam-bia, praise to thee. All one, strong and free.

(T.B.) in the sun.

CHORUS — Sung after 3rd Verse only

(s.) Praise be to God. Bless our great na-
(A.T.) God. na-
(B.) Praise be, praise be, praise be, Zam-bia,

★ The music for this National Anthem was originally written as a hymn tune at Lovedale Mission in Cape Province, South Africa. The tune became well known throughout a large part of southern, central and eastern Africa, and the words were translated into many African languages. Indeed, it came to be popularly known as the Bantu National Anthem. The tune was officially adopted by Tanganyika as its National Anthem on the achievement of Independence in 1961. New words have been specially written for Zambia. A competition was held and these words were produced as a composite version after a study of the ideas and the words of the six leading en-tries in the competition.   By permission of Lovedale Press.

- - tion, Free men we stand___ Un - der the flag___
- - tion, Free men we stand___ Un - der the flag___
Zam - bia, Zam - bia, Free men we stand___ Un - der the flag___

of___ our land.___ Zam - bia, praise to___ thee!___

All one, strong___ and free.___

1. *Lumbanyeni Zambia, no kwanga,*
   Ne cilumba twange tuumfwane,
   Mpalume sha bulwi bwa cine,
   Twaliilubula.
   Twikatane bonse.

2. *Bonse tuli bana ba Africa,*
   Uwasenaminwa na Lesa,
   Nomba bonse twendele pamo,
   Twaliilubula.
   Twikatane bonse.

3. *Fwe lukuta lwa Zambia lonse,*
   Twikatane tubyo mutende,
   Pamo nga lubambe mu mulu,
   Lumbanyeni Zambia.
   Twikatane bonse.

CHORUS (after 3rd verse only)
   Lumbanyeni,
   Lesa, Lesa, wesu,
   Apale calo,
   Zambia, Zambia, Zambia.
   Fwe bantungwa
   Mu luunga lwa calo.
   Lumbanyeni Zambia.
   Twikatane bonse.

Nkosi Sikelel'i Africa

Words and Music by
ENOCH SONTONGA

By permission of Lovedale Press, Cape Province, South Africa.

This anthem has for many years been sung by the Bantu in central and southern Africa. By the Transkei Constitution Act of May 1963 it officially became the National Anthem of the Xhosa-speaking peoples of the Transkei, which is in eastern Cape Province.

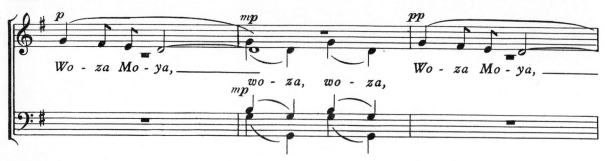

Wo - za Mo - ya,_____ Wo - za Mo - ya,_____
woza, woza,

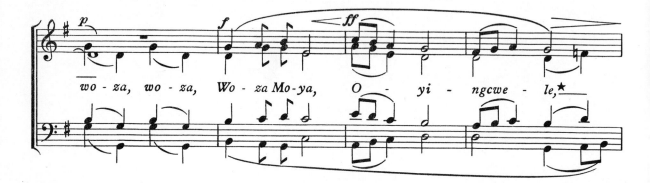

wo - za, wo - za, Wo - za Mo - ya, O - yi - ngcwe - le,★

U - si si - ke - le - le,_____ Ti - na lu - sa - pho - lwa - yo.

Free Translation

God bless Africa,
Let her fame spread far and wide;
Hear our prayer,
May God bless us.
Come, Spirit, come,
Come, Holy Spirit,
Come and bless us, her children.

This song was composed in 1897 and first sung publicly in 1899. The composer died before it was published and his manuscript was eventually borrowed and lost. Some other musical arrangements have become known. Another version, published by Lovedale Press, is slightly different from the above; it is set in the key of B flat, has no repeat and terminates at the asterisk. The National Anthems of Tanzania and Zambia are based on this.

NATIONAL DAYS

AFGHANISTAN	27 May	*Independence Day, 1919*
ALBANIA	11 January	*National Day, 1946*
	29 November	*National Day, 1944*
ALGERIA	5 July	*Independence Day, 1962*
	1 November	*National Day, 1954*
ANDORRA	8 September	*Jungfrau von Meritxell Day (Patron Saint of Andorra)*
ARGENTINE	25 May	*National Day (Anniversary of May Revolution, 1810)*
	9 July	*Independence Day, 1816*
AUSTRALIA	26 January	*Australia Day, 1788*
	25 April	*Anzac Day, 1915*
AUSTRIA	15 May	*Signing of Austrian State Treaty, 1955*
	26 October	*National Day, 1955*
BARBADOS	30 November	*Independence Day, 1966*
BELGIUM	21 July	*National Day, 1831*
BOLIVIA	9 April	*Anniversary of the National Revolution, 1952*
	6 August	*Anniversary of Independence, 1825*
BOTSWANA	30 September	*Independence Day, 1966*
BRAZIL	7 September	*Independence Day, 1822*
BULGARIA	9 September	*National Day, 1944*
BURMA	4 January	*Independence Day, 1948*
	12 February	*Union Day, 1947*
BURUNDI	1 July	*Independence Day, 1962*
CAMBODIA	9 November	*Independence Day, 1945*
CAMEROON	1 January	*Independence Day, 1960*
CANADA	1 July	*Canada Day (Anniversary of Confederation, 1867)*
CENTRAL AFRICAN REPUBLIC	13 August	*Independence Day, 1960*
CEYLON	4 February	*Independence Day, 1948*
CHAD	11 August	*Independence Day, 1960*
CHILE	18 September	*Independence Day, 1810*
CHINA (National)	10 October	*Proclamation of Republic of Dr. Sun Yat-Sen, 1911*
CHINA (Communist)	1 October	*Proclamation of Provisional Constitution, 1949*
COLUMBIA	20 July	*Independence Day, 1810*
CONGO (Brazzaville)	15 August	*Independence Day, 1960*
CONGO (Kinshasa)	30 June	*Independence Day, 1960*
COSTA RICA	15 September	*Independence Day, 1821*
CUBA	20 May	*Independence Day, 1902*
CZECHOSLOVAKIA	28 October	*Foundation of Czechoslovak Republic*
DAHOMEY	1 August	*Independence Day, 1960*
DENMARK	11 March	*Birthday of H.M. King Frederik IX, 1899*
	5 June	*Constitution Day, 1849*
DOMINICAN REPUBLIC	27 February	*Independence Day, 1844*
ECUADOR	10 August	*Independence Day, 1809*
EIRE	17 March	*St. Patrick's Day*
EL SALVADOR	15 September	*Independence Day, 1821*
ENGLAND	23 April	*St. George's Day*
ETHIOPIA	5 May	*Anniversary of the Restoration of Independence, 1941*
	23 July	*Birthday of H.I.M. Haile Selassie I, 1891*

453

FAROE ISLANDS	29 July	*National Day*
FINLAND	6 December	*Independence Day, 1917*
FRANCE	14 July	*National Day (Bastille Day, 1789)*
GABON	17 August	*Independence Day, 1960*
GAMBIA, THE	18 February	*Independence Day, 1965*
GERMANY	17 June	*Day of Unity*
GHANA	6 March	*Independence Day, 1957*
GREECE	25 March	*Independence Day, 1821*
GUATEMALA	15 September	*Independence Day, 1821*
GUINEA	2 October	*Proclamation of the Repuplic, 1958*
GUYANA	26 May	*Independence Day, 1966*
HAITI	1 January	*Independence Day, 1804*
HONDURAS	15 September	*Independence Day, 1821*
HUNGARY	4 April	*Anniversary of the Liberation, 1945*
ICELAND	17 June	*Anniversary of Establishment of the Republic, 1944*
	1 December	*Independence Day, 1918*
INDIA	26 January	*Republic Day, 1950*
	15 August	*Independence Day, 1947*
INDONESIA	17 August	*Independence Day, 1945*
IRAN	5 August	*Constitution Day*
	26 October	*Birthday of H.I.M. Mohammed Reza Shah Pahlevi, 1919*
IRAQ	14 July	*National Day*
ISRAEL	15 May	*Independence Day, 1948*
ITALY	2 June	*Anniversary of Proclamation of the Republic, 1946*
IVORY COAST	7 August	*Independence Day, 1960*
JAMAICA	6 August	*Independence Day, 1962*
JAPAN	3 May	*Constitution Day*
	3 November	*Cultural Day*
JORDAN	25 May	*Independence Day, 1946*
KENYA	12 December	*Independence Day and Republic Day, 1963 and 1964*
KOREA	3 October	*Independence Day, 1948*
KUWAIT	19 June	*National Day, 1961*
LAOS	11 May	*National Day (Constitution Day), 1947*
	19 July	*Independence Day, 1946*
LEBANON	22 November	*Independence Day, 1943*
LESOTHO	4 October	*Independence Day, 1966*
LIBERIA	26 July	*Independence Day, 1847*
LIBYA	24 December	*Independence Day, 1951*
LIECHTENSTEIN	16 August	*Birthday of H.S.H. Prince Franz-Josef II, 1906*
LUXEMBOURG	23 June	*National Day*
MADAGASCAR	26 June	*Proclamation of Independence of the Malagasy Republic, 1960*
MALAWI	6 July	*Independence Day and Republic Day, 1964 and 1966*
MALAYA	31 August	*Malaysia Day*
MALDIVE ISLANDS	7 August	*Independence Day, 1965*
MALI	22 September	*Independence Day, 1960*
MALTA	8 September	*National Day, 1565 and 1940/3*
MAURITANIA	28 November	*Independence Day, 1960*

MEXICO	16 September	*National Day, 1810*
MONACO	19 November	*National Day*
MONGOLIA	11 July	*National Day, 1921*
MOROCCO	7 March	*Independence Day, 1956*
NEPAL	18 February	*National Day, 1952*
NETHERLANDS	30 April	*Birthday of H.M. Queen Juliana, 1909*
NEW ZEALAND	6 February	*New Zealand Day, 1840*
	25 April	*Anzac Day, 1915*
NICARAGUA	15 September	*Independence Day, 1821*
NIGER	3 August	*Independence Day, 1960*
	18 December	*National Day*
NIGERIA	1 October	*Independence Day, 1960*
NORWAY	17 May	*Constitution Day, 1814*
OMAN	18 July	*Oman Day*
PAKISTAN	23 March	*Republic Day, 1956*
	14 August	*Independence Day,1947*
PANAMA	3 November	*Independence Day, 1903*
PARAGUAY	14 May	*Independence Day, 1811*
	25 November	*Constitution Day, 1870*
PERU	28 July	*Independence Day, 1821*
PHILLIPPINES, The	4 July	*Independence Day, 1946*
POLAND	22 July	*Constitution Day, 1952*
PORTUGAL	10 June	*National Day*
ROMANIA	9 May	*National Independence Day, 1877*
	23 August	*Anniversary of the Liberation, 1944*
RWANDA	1 July	*Independence Day, 1962*
SAN MARINO	3 September	*National Day*
SAUDI ARABIA	20 May	*Independence Day, 1927*
	23 September	*National Day, 1964*
SENEGAL	4 April	*Independence Day, 1960*
SIERRA LEONE	27 April	*Independence Day, 1960*
SINGAPORE	9 August	*Independence Day, 1965*
SOMALI	1 July	*Independence Day, 1960*
SOUTH AFRICA	31 May	*Republic Day, 1961*
SOUTHERN YEMEN	30 November	*Independence Day, 1967*
SPAIN	2 May	*Independence Day,*
	18 July	*Labour Day (celebrated as Spanish National Day), 1936*
SUDAN	1 January	*Independence Day, 1956*
SWAZILAND	6 September	*Independence Day, 1948*
SWEDEN	6 June	*National Day, 1809*
SWITZERLAND	1 August	*Anniversary of the Foundation of Confederation, 1291*
SYRIA	17 April	*National Day, 1943*
TANZANIA	26 April	*Tanzanian Union Day, 1964*
	9 December	*Independence Day and Republic Day, 1961 and 1962*
THAILAND	5 December	*National Day*
TOGO	27 April	*Independence Day, 1960*
TRINIDAD AND TOBAGO	31 August	*National Day, 1962*
TUNISIA	1 June	*National Day*
	25 July	*Anniversary of Proclamation of the Republic, 1957*
TURKEY	29 October	*Proclamation of the Republic, 1923*

UGANDA	9 October	*Independence Day, 1962*
U.S.S.R.	7 November	*Anniversary of the October Socialist Revolution, 1917*
UNITED ARAB REPUBLIC	23 July	*Anniversary of the Revolution, 1952*
UNITED STATES OF AMERICA	4 July	*Independence Day, 1776*
	27 November	*Thanksgiving Day, 1621. (This is celebrated the nearest Thursday to 27 November each year)*
UPPER VOLTA	5 August	*Independence Day, 1960*
	11 December	*National Day*
URUGUAY	25 August	*Independence Day, 1825*
VENEZUELA	5 July	*National Day. (Signing of Independence, 1811)*
VIET-NAM	1 November	*National Day, 1963*
WALES	1 March	*St. David's Day*
WESTERN SAMOA	1 January	*Independence Day, 1962*
YUGOSLAVIA	29 November	*National Day*
ZAMBIA	24 October	*Independence Day, 1964*